Farms and Farmers in an Urban Age

L. H. Russwurm

Farms
and Farmers
in an Urban Age

Edward Higbee

The Twentieth Century Fund
New York 1963

Published June 1963
Second printing November 1963
Third printing October 1964

TO Clayton M. Hoff

Conservationist and
Interpreter of the Natural World

Foreword

PROFESSOR Higbee has presented in this volume a picture of the modern farmer different from that which comes down to us from traditional observers. It is different also from that held by most of those shaping today's government policy and by many agricultural economists. We believe it is one, nevertheless, which deserves careful consideration in various quarters — and not least by farmers themselves.

Today's farmer, Professor Higbee argues, is essentially a new man. His work and outlook have been shaped by conditions which did not exist in previous generations. A remnant still carries forward the old ways and traditions, and government policy is largely shaped with the idea of supporting and sustaining this group. But the benefits of such a policy actually go preponderantly to the new farmer, who is a capitalist frequently operating on a large scale, and more in tune with an urban than a rural society.

The reader will find Professor Higbee's theses persuasively argued and supported by ample evidence. The Twentieth Century Fund is grateful to the author for carrying out the work. It believes this volume will stand fittingly with those other studies by which, over the years, it has sought to throw light upon the problems raised by modern agriculture.

AUGUST HECKSCHER, *Director*
The Twentieth Century Fund

41 East 70th Street, New York
March 1963

Acknowledgments

THE AUTHOR is not the only one who takes a risk when he promises to do a piece of research and summarize it in a book. His employer takes a risk by excusing him temporarily from his normal duties and his sponsors take a risk by supporting him while he does the job. Without such encouragements one could only dream about what he wishes he had time to read about, inquire about, and think about. It is therefore a pleasure to acknowledge that I am first of all indebted to the University of Rhode Island and my students for granting me a leave of absence to do the research which this book required, and to the Twentieth Century Fund for supporting it.

Many persons of good will contributed in various ways to make the work itself a pleasant task. It was owing to the cooperation of scores of farmers in nearly every part of the United States that I was able to get some clues as to how the technological revolution in agriculture affects them personally and what, as a consequence, is uppermost in their minds. To all of them and to the many field specialists of the United States Department of Agriculture who offered every courtesy in the course of my travels, I am most grateful. Among them I have gained new friends whom I hope I shall meet again.

Putting a book together could be a frustrating experience without skilled help to gather and process an immense amount of published data. I am indeed indebted to those who lightened my tasks in these respects. In particular, I want to thank Holly Bellere for maintaining the reference files in an efficient manner. I am grateful also to Sara Sklar for checking statistical data, to Mary Garrigan for secretarial assistance, and to Katharine Beyer for editing.

E. H.

Mooresfield Farm
Kingston, Rhode Island

Contents

Farms and Farmers in an Urban Age

Introduction

AMERICAN AGRICULTURE never had it so good — but a lot of farmers were never so scared. The fast growing population in cities and suburbs is buying more than ever before and farmers are knocking each other out in a scramble for the market. In 1935 there were 6.8 million farms. Now there are less than 3.7 million. By 1980 there may be less than 1 million. As poorer farmers drop out of the race for survival their lands are consolidated by a smaller, abler group of operators who spend more money to buy more machinery to raise bigger crops. The fate of the displaced losers is for the congested city to worry about for that is where most of agriculture's cast-offs are going. The winners are taking the wide open country to themselves and are living higher on the hog.

Today the top 3 per cent of all farms produce more than the bottom 78 per cent. In between these extremes is a group of 19 per cent whose owners are in good shape. Farms of 1,000 acres and over possessed only 28 per cent of all agricultural land in 1930. By 1959 these big units, which were only 3.7 per cent of all farms, had acquired 49 per cent of all the land and their average size had reached 4,048 acres — more than 6 square miles apiece. America's 100,000 top-drawer farms produce 31.5 per cent of all crops and livestock. In real estate alone these enterprises are worth, on the average, nearly a quarter of a million dollars each ($220,000) and the average annual value of their sales is $94,000.

At the other end of the production line there are 2.9 million farms which have an average annual value of sales of $3,000. The

3

700,000 farms in between have annual sales that average $18,000. As some farms get bigger and others liquidate, the federal programs for agriculture expand and the Department of Agriculture itself puts on weight. In 1935 the federal budget for agriculture was less than $1 billion. In 1962 it was over $7 billion, a sum exceeded only by expenditures for defense and interest on the national debt.

If there is any regret that the small scale farm which counted on family labor as its chief asset is passing from the scene, a similar regret might be expressed about the passing of small scale family enterprise in manufacturing, in shopkeeping, and in services. Maybe what is mourned is the passing of that old-fashioned small scale America in which family labor enterprise was the rule in town as in the country. But a social institution cannot live out of context and the old context has been demolished by the growth of mass populations. Smallness is out; bigness is in. New systems of mass production are needed to satisfy the mass needs of a vastly multiplied and urbanized humanity. The nation has grown to new dimensions and must be measured by a new yardstick.

The small farmer can no longer establish contact with the small consumer on a scale required to feed the population. Food must be assembled by the trainload rather than by the wagonload, and transported across the continent rather than across a township. This calls for a new gigantism in production and in distribution. A few little farmers may survive by lying between the rails as the freights thunder by, but they are becoming as rare as old-fashioned butchershops in an age of supermarkets.

It is hard for the nation to face up to the fact that throughout the economy it is more profitable to employ capital than to employ people. A new technology and modern tax policy have made it smart business to use machines rather than men wherever possible. Machines can be depreciated through the fast write-off — a gain. Men must be pensioned — a loss. Machines get better and better; men do not improve much. When capital and men compete for employment the shrewd entrepreneur will hire capital because he can predict more accurately what it will do and what it will cost. On the farm this means that a family which is long on labor but short on capital has become obsolete as a production unit.

Since agriculture has developed a highly effective production machine and its unneeded human resources have been shifted to the city America has been confronted with two kinds of surpluses. In the country there is a surplus of food. In the city there is a surplus of labor. To relieve these twin problems two forms of public subsidy have been required — one to compensate farmers for food they cannot sell, the other to compensate the unemployed for labor they cannot expend. Thus far the federal budget to relieve the problem of farm surpluses has been more generous than the federal budget to relieve the urban problem of surplus people. This, in part, is due to the influence of rural spokesmen who contend that the problem of human surpluses is one for local governments to resolve with local tax funds while the problem of farm surpluses is one for the national treasury.

To consider the problem of farm surpluses apart from the problem of human surpluses is to ignore the fact that the two are related in so far as it is more economical to raise food by the capital-intensive methods of the new agriculture rather than by the labor-intensive methods of the old style family farm. This book tells what has happened to the farm as the result of the substitution of capital for people. Other segments of the economy are undergoing parallel changes. American society has entered an era of mass population increase at the very moment when man appears to have become obsolete.

Chapter 1

The Technological
Revolution

OLD STYLE

Now that American agriculture has been invaded by the com-
puter, radioactive elements, and the credit card it is somewhat un-
usual to find a farmer who plows with horses and thinks that one
way to make money is not to spend it. Such a man, however, is
Valentine Y. Byler of Pennsylvania who came to the attention of
an Internal Revenue agent when he neglected to pay his Social Security assessments.[1] Mr. Byler is an Amishman of the Old Order
faith, and Old Order Amishmen scorn the government's Social Security program because they feel it is the Lord's will that members
of a family living on a family farm should care for one another to
the end of their days. These thrifty folk are convinced that one way
to keep farm and family together and to avoid public support is to
rely upon horsepower which can be raised at home on home-
grown hay. Store-bought tractors that run on store-bought gasoline
are the devil's own temptation. These being his convictions, Mr.
Byler was momentarily stymied when the Man-from-Washington
flashed legal papers, attached his work horses, and sold them to pay

7

up his federal retirement arrears. If at that point one more old-fashioned son of the soil had dropped out of agriculture no one would have been surprised. However, the Amishman, abetted by friendly members of his sect, borrowed another team, plowed his fields, and waited for the rains to reward him.

Talk with any Amishman and he will declare that his way of farming is a natural to beat the mounting pressures that today drive families of modest means off the land. Talk with a statistician who knows census data and he will say that the chances for survival of those who cling to old ideas and old methods are rather slim. Farming has become a high-speed business rather than a philosophy or a way of life. And it is no longer a dependable social security institution. The farmer who expects to lead the pack has taken off his overalls to put on his business suit for a trip to Washington and a talk with his congressman.

CHANGE

American agriculture is beyond the halfway mark in its second major technological revolution. During the first of these upheavals on the rural landscape, between 1850 and 1910, the Indians of the Great Plains were confined to reservations, Negro slavery was abolished, and the total of farms increased from 1.4 million to 6.4 million, most of them owned and operated by a single family.[2] These changes occurred during the revolution of the mule and the horse when animal power on a mass scale was harnessed to a marvelous assortment of tillage implements, and man in the United States was released from the hoe, the sickle, and the fear of hunger. Now agriculture is undergoing a second period of change — the revolution of science, mechanics, and heavy capital investment. While it has not as yet done away with the family farm it has gone a long way toward getting rid of the farm family.

In 1935 American farm units reached an all-time peak of 6.8 million. Since then there has been a precipitous drop in numbers. By

1961 there were left only 3.7 million. Within another decade or two this figure will very likely be cut back to 1.4 million. Since this was the starting point in 1850, the cycle will then be complete. Eventually, as the story is told of how this nation grew and changed, the era of the small family-homestead will appear brief. With its demise any influence which widespread security in land ownership may have had upon the American psyche will cease to exist. A hundred years ago, when there were only about 32 million people in the United States, about 65 per cent of them lived on farms. By 1980 probably less than 5 per cent of the people will live and work on the soil. Although most of the land will continue to be devoted to husbandry, the newer ways of rural life will bear little resemblance to those of the past. The culture, even more than the agriculture, of 185 million Americans is in flux.

In 1800, during the time of the sickle, an average of 56 hours of labor were required to produce an acre of wheat. By 1880, when the horse-drawn reaper was widely employed, it took 20 man-hours to grow and harvest an acre of wheat. Today on the Great Plains less than 2 hours of labor will do the job and do it better. A single mechanical cotton picker can gather as much fiber as forty pairs of human hands. Go into the country on a bright July day and there one man may be seen to bale and load 10 tons of hay in an hour while sitting down. Twenty years ago two men working with pitchforks could not have done that much in a whole afternoon. Just how many hours are saved by a modern harvester that tops and pulls an acre of radishes in an hour is any weekend gardener's guess. This is the machine which made the lowly radish one of the supermarket's best year-round buys. By 1910, when horse-drawn implements had taken over a substantial part of corn production, 147 man-hours were required to raise 100 bushels. This was quite an improvement over the 344 man-hours needed in the hand-hoe days of 1800, but today a few exceptional farmers in the corn belt raise 100 bushels of corn with less than 4 hours of labor.[3] Better seeds, pesticides, and more fertilizers, as well as machinery, have made this progress possible. The improved efficiency of modern agriculture is as fabulous as the conquest of outer space, and it is far more significant for the welfare of humankind.

The number of horses and mules on American farms reached a peak of almost 27 million in 1917. By 1960 the total had dropped to 3 million. In the same span of time the number of tractors increased from 51,000 to nearly 5 million.[4] Now aircraft are considered the most efficient spreaders of fertilizers and pesticides where large acreages require quick, uniform treatment. Because rice fields are often flooded, growers of this crop are particularly inclined to be airborne. They hire planes to seed, fertilize, and spray pesticides, and when the crop is about to ripen they hasten maturity by spraying hormones from the air. Rice growers have also discovered that planes are more effective than scarecrows at dispersing blackbirds; when birds become a problem a farmer may place a call to the nearest air service to buzz them. So many operations are done by commercial pilots on a custom basis that some people claim rice plantations are run by telephones rather than by farmers.

In 1961 the irrigated fields of southern California got a glimpse of the first self-propelled lettuce packers which cost over $20,000 each and pack 600 boxes of lettuce per hour right in the field. These mobile "factories" which lumber down the lush green rows like dinosaurs carry ten girls and a boxing crew. The girls wrap and seal each head of lettuce in a plastic cover while the boxing crews pack them for trucks that follow. The trucks carry the cartons to cooling plants at rail sidings and within a few hours the chilled lettuce is on its way across the continent.

For a long time it was thought that the culture of tree and bush fruits could not be mechanized but now there are dozens of operational models that prune and pick. Modern orchards look like giant hedgerows after they have been trimmed by buzz saws mounted on hydraulic beams transported by tractors. Some fruit growers have reduced field labor forces at harvest time to one-tenth of former requirements by using mechanical tree shakers and fruit catchers which are wrapped around the trees like firemen's life nets.

PARADOX

Mechanization in farming brings about the same economic and social changes that it does in industry. Already it has eliminated the need for cheap, illiterate hired labor in the production of corn and wheat and, to a considerable extent, cotton. Now mechanical devices are taking over jobs in fruit and vegetable production where some of the most primitive and degrading conditions for human living in rural America still prevail. While labor efficiency and living standards have improved more rapidly in agricultural areas than in cities in recent years, some of the nation's poorest people are yet to be found in rural districts where social and economic progress took a detour. It is ironic that within that very segment of the economy which suffers from the overproduction of food there are farmers and farmhands who suffer from malnutrition because they cannot afford to eat properly. For these persons more progress cannot come soon enough.

One of the strangest features of modern American agriculture is that farm income stagnated during years when technical efficiency made some of its greatest gains. In the decade 1948–57 production per man-hour on farms increased 48.6 per cent while the improvement in other industries was only 25.5 per cent. During the 1950's the average annual increase in production per worker was slightly above 6 per cent in agriculture. Outside of agriculture it was under 3 per cent. At the end of 1960 capital investment for each worker in agriculture was $21,300 compared with $15,900 for each worker in other industries. In 1960 one farmer produced enough food for 26 persons whereas in 1940 his efforts fed only 11 persons. In 1959 the average income of all farm families from agriculture was $2,875 while that of all urban families was $5,911. In that same year 18 per cent of all farm families had total incomes of less than $1,000 whereas only 3 per cent of all urban families had such inadequate incomes.[5]

Something must be wrong with this story. How could anything doing so well be so badly off? It does not make sense.

TWO EXTREMES

The dreary picture developed by these statistics is both true and false. It is mathematically correct but it is deceptive because it lumps all farmers together, and it credits farm families with farm income only. If the non-farm earnings of farm operator families are included, then it turns out that their average net income for 1959 was $5,115. The fact is that quite a few tillers of the soil do extraordinarily well even without off-farm earnings. These are the big-spending, modernized, full-time, professional farmers. (Table 10.) Others at the tail end of the barnyard pecking order are called farmers only because the Bureau of the Census and the Department of Agriculture do not know exactly where to cut off a factory worker who is a part-time farmer or a farmer who is a part-time factory worker and just plain unemployed most of the time. In some rural sections underemployment and seasonal unemployment is as serious as joblessness in distressed urban areas. Yet tens of thousands of rural indigents are called farmers even though they cannot raise enough to feed themselves properly.

It is the great weight of poverty at the lower levels that makes all agriculture look sick in statistics when in reality the upper crust which produces most of the food could pass its physical any day in the week and be classified 1–A. In public discussions about the ills of husbandry a distinction seldom is made between what is a social problem of wider scope and what pertains strictly to the agricultural economy. Because coal mines are shut down in West Virginia the public does not assume that all industry is in a slump, yet similar deductions are made with respect to agriculture. In 1959, 2.2 million operators of 61 per cent of all American farms averaged *five times* more income from work away from their farms than they did from work on them. Most of these people did not earn much either place. Furthermore their marketed production was only 13 per cent of all farm output in 1959.[6] This being the case, the question might be raised whether these persons should be classified as farmers when the problems of agriculture are being considered.

There is widespread indigence in rural areas because many people called farmers are not financially able to meet the costs of technological improvement. This is not the fault of the people concerned. They have simply been by-passed by a technology too rich for their blood. While some operators can make it on credit cards others have to scrape along on money. The latter keep falling farther and farther behind. Most city factory workers long ago became reconciled to the fact that they could not own and operate their own shops. Now it is the farmer who faces the realities of an industrial age.

No reasonable headway can be made in reshaping national policy toward agriculture until it is recognized that the players at the top and the players at the bottom are not in the same league and the spread between them is getting wider. Eighty-seven per cent of the value of all farm products sold in 1959 was accounted for by 1.4 million farms, or 39 per cent of the total.[6] If the other 2.2 million farms were to go out of business by 1969 their output would not be missed. The big question is how will all these people who are not needed in agriculture find ways to make a living elsewhere? Already city slums harbor hundreds of thousands of rural refugees, many on welfare rolls.

CITY JOBS

The only real solution to agriculture's major social problem is more city jobs for people who would gladly give up farm pursuits if there were a decent alternative. As it is, the federal money being poured into agriculture does not keep farm and farm family together as press releases say it is intended to do. The years of biggest federal spending in agriculture have been the years of steepest decline in the numbers of farms and farmers. They have also been years of rising surpluses. The two trends are connected. As the less efficient farmers drop out, their lands are taken over by the more efficient, and bigger crops are produced on the same acres.

In 1959 Senator John J. Williams of Delaware examined the record and reported that three of the largest farm corporations in the country together collected more price support money than all of the farmers in Pennsylvania, New Jersey, Delaware, and Maryland combined. Editorialized the *Philadelphia Inquirer,* "Principal beneficiaries of the U. S. farm program are the big farmers and crop storage operators . . . Fifty-six per cent of the nation's farmers are in the small and marginal category but they get less than 7 per cent of Government handouts."[7] What the Senator and the *Inquirer* observed was not a coincidence. The system is designed that way. Some individual farm operators have collected over $1 million a year in federal price support loans. Acreage controls scarcely affect the really fluid manipulators. When the government cuts allotments on properties owned by those with easy access to credit, they simply go out on the real estate market and buy more land with allotments and grow as much as ever.

Cotton is a surplus crop like wheat, so it is grown under a quota system designed to restrict production to what can be a profitable level. A man may grow cotton without penalty only if he has a government quota and stays within it. A couple of decades ago most cotton was produced by sharecroppers with "twenty acres and a mule" because twenty acres were about all a family and a mule could handle. Since that time hundreds of thousands of sharecroppers have dropped out of agriculture in the "Old South" and their federal acreage allotments have gone westward to the irrigated areas of Texas, Arizona, and California. (Table 10.) There these official permits have been acquired by big-scale mechanized operators.

"We've lost them forever" was the complaint of a South Carolinian who felt that the allotments in question should have been kept on deposit in his state until progressive local growers could have expanded enough to use them. However, there is an insistent transcontinental demand for cotton permits with no small amount of political pressure involved, so they do not remain orphaned long. An allotment for twenty acres which might be unprofitable to a mule farmer becomes gilt-edged when it is combined with about fifteen or twenty more like it and put under irrigation and machine cultivation.

TRANSMUTATION

The nice things that can happen to a person with a fistful of adopted cotton allotments were clarified recently for the public by farm-born Billie Sol Estes of west Texas. With the help of a number of friends in and out of government, the persuasive Mr. Estes was able to corral 3,123 acres of official cotton allotments. To use them called for a lot of fertilizer, so while he was collecting the permits Mr. Estes also went into the fertilizer business. In addition he picked up a half dozen grain elevators in which he stored surplus grain for the federal government at a nicer profit than most growers could get out of raising it. His activities are said to have reached such a grandiose scale that Mr. Estes was able to secure a loan of $22 million on liquid ammonia fertilizer tanks which did not exist.[8]

Just as a zealous agent of the law once descended upon a smaller agriculturist to pick up a few obsolete horses in the interests of Social Security, federal investigators eventually descended upon farmer Estes. When this happened he pleaded with his creditors to cover him in order that he might pay up. He is said to have confided to a principal mortgagee: "Without the grain business [which brought in between $6 and $8 million a year] and the cotton deals, my house of cards will collapse."[9] But the boom fell and the first assets to be impounded along with Mr. Estes were the cotton allotments which would have been enough for 150 family farmers in the good old mule days of 1940.

It is a strange world when something which is worthless in small denominations becomes the taproot of fortune when it is consolidated by a smart organizer. But so it is on the contemporary stage of high-speed American agriculture, and that is why this segment of the economy is more like Alice's wonderland than anything described in the *Farmer's Almanack*.

CAPITAL GAIN

The urban taxpayer often gets steamed up over congressional subsidies to agriculture — especially when he notes that farm real estate seems to be on a perpetual joyride of inflation. The city resident and grocery buyer naturally wonders why it is that the market price of farm property keeps going up if it is really true that agriculture is in trouble. If he suspects that the sob stories are partly soap opera and that capital is going into agriculture because a lot of farms are good investments, he is right. It is, of course, a fact that the labor income from farm operations in recent years has not been anything to brag about, but inflation in property values is the big story.

For those more interested in capital gains than in current income, agriculture has been a natural. In 1950 the average value of an acre of farm land was $65. By 1960 it had reached $120. The net increase in real estate worth during those ten years was $53.8 billion, or about $10,000 for each farm that existed in 1950.[10] Owners who simply held onto their fields thereby acquired considerable wealth. Those who sold out almost invariably made a capital gain. The capital gain on farm real estate between 1950 and 1960 averaged 8.5 per cent per year.[11] "Why," asks the man in town, "should I dig into my sock to help increase the farmer's equity in property?" While farm mortgage debt increased only $6.5 billion between 1940 and 1961 the value of all farm assets went up $119 billion. This is hardly a symptom of serious illness. The 1961 farm mortgage debt was only 10.4 per cent of farm real estate values.[12] Few city people are so solvent.

Not everybody in agriculture has been raking in capital gains like hay in July sunshine. The farm people who have had the roughest time in recent years have been helped the least by federal price supports and other programs. Hired hands, custom workers, migrant laborers, and part-time help, who together constitute about 45 per cent of all persons engaged in agriculture (footnote a, Table 12), have not done well because they do not own real estate. The 20 per cent of all farm operators who are tenants also have not enjoyed the capital gains that have supplemented the low labor incomes of owner-operator families. In many areas, even in good times, the value of farm labor never reached $1.00 an hour. While farm owners strive for federal minimum price guarantees they are generally opposed to minimum wage legislation for field hands and migrant workers. Again the urbanite might inquire why it is that his taxes and the government's solicitude go to guarantee the prices of crops but no serious effort is made to see that the producers of those crops reciprocate so their hired hands might buy a respectable share of the city's manufactured goods.

If he is not naïve the urbanite should know by now that the nation's agricultural program is not designed to help just anyone who calls himself a farmer. Rather it is designed to bolster the agricultural economy so as to make farming profitable for those able to invest fresh capital in it. A healthy, expanding, and profitable farm economy is the first concern of the policy maker and politician. As long as the prices of corn, wheat, cotton, and milk are sufficient to please some technically advanced producers little sleep is lost over the fate of those who simply offer their labor to agriculture or who own substandard family farms with antique machinery. President Dwight D. Eisenhower recognized this aspect of price support programs when he commented to Congress about the 5.4 million farms which existed in 1950: "The chief beneficiaries of our price support policies have been the 2 million larger,

highly mechanized farming units which produce about 85 per cent
of our agricultural output. The individual production of the remaining farms, numbering about 3.5 million, is so small that the
farmer derives little benefit from price supports."[13] However, government policy did not change appreciably and ten years later another 1.7 million farms failed to appear in the census.*

THE OTHER SIDE

Before the urban taxpayer begins to feel too sorry for himself he
should look at another side of the farm ledger. Nobody in the
world is fed for a smaller part of his take-home pay than the American grocery buyer. Most people elsewhere in the world spend at
least half of their disposable incomes for food. In Western Europe
food costs are 30 to 45 per cent of spendable wages. In Russia they
are 55 per cent. In parts of Asia and Latin America some people
pay almost everything they earn for food and even then they are
badly nourished.[14] The real cost of food in any country increases
as the proportion of farmers increases within the total labor force.
Food costs are highest where 90 per cent or more of the people
work the soil. In the United States only 8 per cent of the population lives on the farm and food costs are less than 20 per cent of the
average family budget.[14]

In underdeveloped countries, where food costs absorb the greater
share of wages, yields are usually low. The peasants and peons try
to make up for a lack of machinery, fertilizers, pesticides, and good
seeds by applying more human toil to more acres of poor land. But
it takes more than sweat to make crops grow well. The more people who are tied up in such futile agriculture, the poorer the country, the poorer its diet, and the more that diet costs in terms of
average incomes in those countries.

---

* The census definition of a farm changes from time to time so figures are not
always comparable. Allowing for units dropped for this reason, the net decline was
1.5 million. A more realistic definition of a farm in the next census would eliminate
two-fifths of the present total.

The machines, seeds, chemicals, and technical knowledge used on fields from Maine to California are not secret. They were preceded by extensive programs of research, experimentation, and development by agencies of state and national Departments of Agriculture, the land-grant colleges, private business firms and individuals. They are available to anyone in the world who will pay for them, but as yet only the first class American farmer has been able and willing to spend heavily for these products of modern science and technology. Only he has reaped their full benefits, to his own profit and that of the urban consumer. While it costs tax money to subsidize surplus production in the United States, the net cost to the food-eating public is probably less than it would have been if the technological revolution had been retarded for lack of a profit incentive.

HARD SELL

Some time ago a man, neatly dressed in a business suit, pushed a shopping basket up and down the aisles of a supermarket in Arlington, Virginia. He was after groceries but he was also seeking public opinion, which made his mission somewhat hazardous. Attempting a *tour de force* in salesmanship, this dignified executive in horn-rimmed glasses began to speak before an assemblage of housewives lined up at the check-out counter. "I came over today to visit with some of you ladies to tell you food really is the cheapest thing we can buy," was his opening gambit. While a dozen female mouths gaped, the male in their midst asked, "Did you know food prices are lower than other things, compared with prices ten years ago?" One housewife, who ten years previously probably spent her allowance on eye shadow rather than on baby food, replied, "Well, I don't know. Seems to me everything's gone up, not down." The tailored executive did not wince; this was exactly the reaction he had expected. "That's why I'm here today," said the new Secretary of Agriculture, Orville L. Freeman. Then he proceeded to tell the budget-harried housewives that they were getting more and more food for a smaller and smaller slice of their husbands' pay checks. Just as the charm was beginning to work, a red-faced man behind a cart containing three loaves of bread and a bottle of milk blurted out, "You're feeding these people a lot of bunk." The Secretary did not quarrel, for he was out not to offend his public but to win sympathy for the man on the diesel tractor. He passed out leaflets to explain his cause. Then, when the supply was exhausted, he climbed into his car and drove back across the Potomac.[15]

A look at cold facts shows that the Secretary of Agriculture did not "feed" his public "a lot of bunk." It is perfectly true that the average American consumer never has been so well fed for such a small percentage of his pay check. However, averages hide the fact that one-sixth of the population exists on submarginal incomes and people in this group do not earn average factory pay. Even 40 per cent of the earnings of some of these people will not buy them a decent diet. An hour at average industrial employment bought 2.2 pounds of round steak in 1960 compared with 1.2 pounds in 1929. A family living on an average factory wage could buy 8.8 quarts of milk in 1960 with an hour's work that would have bought 3.9 quarts in 1929. The number of oranges that could be purchased rose even more during this period: from 1.3 dozen to 3.1 dozen.[16] Between 1944 and 1959 the nation's annual per capita consumption of meat, fish, and poultry increased 10 per cent, while that of potatoes dropped 30 per cent.[17] In general the purchase of better quality foods has risen while that of poorer quality foods has declined.

During the decade of the 1950's, America's average take-home pay jumped 59 per cent. By comparison the cost of housing rose 32 per cent, transportation climbed 46 per cent, and medical care increased by 57 per cent. In the same period of time the nation's food bill went up only 15 per cent.[18] The net income per farm operator rose 11 per cent. In 1950 the food producer got about half of the consumer's food dollar. By 1960 his share has dropped to 40 cents, while 60 cents remained with the processing and marketing services. Out of the 40 cents that the farmer received he paid 24 cents to those who sold him machines, chemicals, and other services.

An hour of farm labor now produces four times as much as it did in 1919–21. Crop production per acre is up 65 per cent and output per breeding animal is up 88 per cent. Today every person employed in agriculture is backstopped by two others in business either to service farms with machines, chemicals, and other supplies or to market what the farmer produces.[19] Gross farm income in 1960 was $38 billion. Of this amount the operator as landlord, laborer, and investor kept $11.6 billion. Those who serviced the farm received $26.0 billion. The nation's total bill for the products of agriculture was about $97 billion.

As the Honorable A. Willis Robertson said before the United States Senate in February, 1962, a ridiculous feature of today's expanding prosperity is that a key man — the person who actually grows the nation's crops and raises its livestock — gets an average of 84 cents an hour for his labor while industrial workers average $2.36 an hour.[21] One corn-hog grower in Ohio with a $300,000 farm recently remarked, "When I'm on my tractor I'm worth no more than my hired hand."

There are plenty of owner-operators on marginal farms who do all their own work because they cannot afford to hire anybody else. These operators should not expect to earn more than a farm hand's wage for their physical labor. It has been farm operators themselves who have established the low rates for manual labor in agriculture through their opposition to minimum wage legislation. When the owners of small family-operated farms compete with other owners who have hired help they compete with the cheapest labor in the country, including the imported Latin American peace corps of half a million Mexican *braceros* and West Indian *macheteros* who are scattered around the United States from Connecticut to Arizona.

The low value of ordinary work in agriculture induces hundreds of thousands of today's marginal landowners to take town

jobs whenever they can get them. They become commuters when
they find a chance to work city hours for city pay at city jobs. That
routine has it all over country hours for country pay at country
jobs. Lack of city opportunity keeps a lot of farmers on the land
who would like nothing better than to get off it. (Table 10.)

SOLUTIONS

Stanley Yankus, a rebel Michigan farmer, raised 35 acres of
wheat on a small farm at a time when he had permission to raise
only 15 under the government's quota system, and in consequence
he received a $5,072 fine. In protest he sold his place and emigrated
to Australia with his family. There he bought a three-bedroom
suburban home and settled down to a comfortable living as a
clerk. Things are cheaper in Australia and the life "down under"
appeals to Mr. Yankus because the government does not restrict
his chosen economic activity. When interviewed about his new environment, he declared himself to be pleased, adding that his children were doing well in school and "Mrs. Yankus, with her new
home, is happier now than at any time since we left Michigan."[22]
Stanley Yankus knew that to have a future a small farmer must
grow a little more every year. He just did not do it in the proper
manner.

Without an ever larger capital investment and an expanding
acreage it is impossible to get the most advantage from the use of
the latest machinery, superior livestock, or improved varieties of
seeds. Mass production reduces unit costs and that is the secret of
success. Professor R. H. Blosser of Ohio State University has determined that the costs of growing corn can average $61 per acre on a
160 acre farm, but only $54 per acre on a 640 acre farm.[23] This dif-
ference could put one man out of business while paying a profit to
another. One way to get more government allotments of the sort
that Stanley Yankus needed is to buy someone else's farm and add
it to one's own: the allotments go with the farm.

If a man lacks capital or the nerve to borrow for expansion, he is finished. If he is astute, he will develop a credit reputation by borrowing for current operational expenses. A leading farm journal says that today it takes 75 to 80 cents cash outlay for each dollar of eventual gross income.[24] Operational loans should be repaid promptly once crops are sold. The successful farmer will put his own profits into capital equipment and thereby raise his credit rating for even heavier production loans. It has recently become common practice for banks in the corn belt to open an "Operational Credit Line" of $10,000 for their certified customers. The latter simply draw against these loans for current expenses and repay out of sales. Good managers find this facilitates expansion. The aggressive credit policies of California's Bank of America probably have had as much to do with that state's agricultural boom as has political assistance in irrigation development. The rest of the country will not catch up for quite a while, although it has learned a good lesson by observing California's methods.

BIG JOHN

When a man gets big enough and the banks will support him, even stiff government penalties may not stifle his impulse to produce as much as possible. At least that was true in the case of Jack A. Harris, the man reputed to have paid the highest fine ever assessed by the federal government — $965,595 for planting 4,600 acres to cotton without official allotments.[25] Mr. Harris, a living legend in the Southwest, is the owner of at least five agricultural corporations: three that specialize in cotton farming, a cotton gin, and a cattle feed lot with capacity for 4,500 head of feeders. He shuttles around California and Arizona in a private plane to supervise his various enterprises. It was in 1957 that Jack Harris made his biggest play to publicize what a really efficient cotton grower could do if not restrained by government controls.

Mr. Harris rented 4,600 acres of land near Gila Bend, Arizona with the expectation that he could produce 2¼ bales per acre with a market value of 34 cents per pound. He calculated that he could raise this cotton by his streamlined mass production system for 15½ cents per pound, pay the government a fine of 18½ cents and break even. To take all this risk to come out even would hardly make sense to anyone but Jack Harris. However, up his sleeve he had another 5,000 acres of his own which he could put in cotton without penalty because those acres had lawful allotments. Just as a bit of a hedge Mr. Harris put 1,666 acres of this land in the government's soil bank in order to collect a federal bonus of $209,701 for not planting them. The remainder of his cotton fields he planted. Subtracting the federal bonus from the federal fine his net loss to the government amounted to $755,894. As things turned out, the weather was not cooperative in 1954, so the yields on the Harris cotton farms were somewhat disappointing. When he had about completed his harvest, Mr. Harris was asked about his prospects. "I didn't expect to make a lot of money," he replied, "but I didn't expect to lose, either. I wanted to make a point."[25] Apparently he did, for he is still in business and many in the Southwest wish that they had Jack Harris' nerve and other assets.

BETTER PLANTS AND FERTILIZERS

The technological revolution in agriculture, which has resulted in surplus production and in surplus farmers, is partly genetic and chemical. Better plants and better animals as well as advanced knowledge about feeding them both have made it profitable to use better machines. While the new machines may reduce unit costs by mass production, the mass itself is possible only because better germ plasm and better nutrition are also there. Plants as well as animals must be fed for maximum growth. There is a physiological limit to the increases in yields which can be obtained by work alone. This fact is well known by those in backward parts of the world who labor with machete and sickle. Good seed does not result in miracles of production unless the soil is fertilized. The achievements of modern agriculture are the consequence of a complex chain of scientific discoveries and technological advances.

If a farmer disregards any link his crop may be a failure. That is why the example of American excellence in farming has not been copied widely elsewhere in the world. The agricultural achievement of this country, no less than its industrial ability, is the product of the total economic and social environment. It does not stand alone and cannot be exported as some diplomats have dreamed that it might be.

In 1949 the average yield of corn per acre in the United States was 38 bushels. By 1959 it was up to 51 bushels. In the corn belt average yields in 1961 were 67 bushels per acre. On specialized cash-grain farms the average yield was 86 bushels per acre. Now new hybrid seeds are coming out of university experimental plots which are superior to anything even dreamed of, except by the geneticists who breed them. A 100 bushel per acre average for the corn belt is a fair prospect for 1970. The new corns have a genetic potential for production which is between 25 and 50 bushels per acre above that of any corns known to the farmers of 1961. Present types of seed can utilize efficiently about 90 pounds per acre of the essential element nitrogen. The new varieties will efficiently convert 200 pounds of nitrogen per acre into plant tissue through more vigorous growth. If the American chemical industry could not supply cheap nitrogen in almost unlimited amounts, the farmer could not benefit as much by the remarkable advance in corn genetics.

On what is called "God's Little Acre" in Prentiss County, Mississippi, two teen-age boys, Lamar and Linden Ratliff, established a world corn production record of 304 bushels per acre in 1955. Since then the young Ratliffs have tried in vain to surpass their own achievement. In 1961 they came close with 283 bushels. That year they applied 38 tons of manure, a ton of concentrated 14-14-14 fertilizer,* and a ton of nitrate of ammonia to just that one acre of ground. They also irrigated it. The Ratliff corn is grown on the same plot that the boys' father first planted to corn over thirty

---

* 14-14-14 fertilizer is fertilizer which contains 14 per cent nitrogen (N), 14 per cent phosphorus (P_2O_5), and 14 per cent potassium (K_2O).

years ago. Every year until the boys were able to take care of it the father obtained higher and higher yields by giving it more and more fertilizer and attention. The field became a hobby. Now this one-acre plot has become the talk of farmers all over the country. Father Paul Ratliff once remarked, "I remember working this field and not getting a trailerful." In recent years his sons have harvested more than five trailerfuls from that single plot. In the past harvest day at "God's Little Acre" has been a county celebration. Folks have converged on the homestead from miles around. Mrs. Ratliff has provided a huge free meal and county farm agent W. T. Smith has acted as official weigher. Technicians at Mississippi State University have run moisture tests to make the yield official.[27] What surprises lie in store for Prentiss County when the young Ratliffs get hold of the new souped-up hybrids is anybody's guess.

What is happening to corn is happening to wheat, to peanuts, and to sugar cane; in fact it is happening to azaleas, roses, and practically every other economic plant. In humid areas where drought is not a limiting factor the growers of wheat thought they did well years ago when they harvested 20 bushels per acre. Today 40 and 50 bushel yields are common in the Midwest. Denmark led the world in 1959 with an average national harvest of 66 bushels. Now plant breeders at the University of Washington have produced an average of 140 bushels per acre and on one experimental plot they obtained 152 bushels per acre.[28] In 1960 the average yield of potatoes was 9 tons, but the champion potato grower of Pennsylvania had an average harvest of over 23 tons in 1961. Potato production has become such a highly specialized and highly concentrated operation that the major portion of the total United States crop is now supplied by 6,492 leading growers.[29]

SUPERIOR ANIMALS

The livestock side of farming has been revolutionized by new concepts of breeding and feeding. The old notion that purebreds were tops has been assailed by hybrid vigor. Crosses are the fashion and performance testing through progeny now is the popular way to determine the superiority of an animal. The carcass at the packing house and the size of the feed bill are more important than appearance in the show ring. Conformation as a standard for judging the best of class is out of date except at pet shows and at Atlantic City. At one of Oklahoma State University's demonstration farms a Swine Evaluation Station, or "Hogs' Hall of Fame," has been established to test the caliber of boars through the performance of their progeny. Pigs in lots of six from different sows but sired by the same boar are compared with similar lots of pigs sired by other boars. The pigs are comfortably housed, fed the same prime ration, and given temperature-controlled water. All they have to do is enjoy life and grow. When they reach 201 pounds their careers as research assistants come to an end. Their carcasses are dressed and measured for quality of loins, hams, bacon, and the total amount of all lean cuts. Then days on feed are compared as well as the total amount of feed consumed. By analysis of the performance of the offspring the genetic influence of the father is determined. The best males get a chance to exercise their talents under the most encouraging circumstances, while the inferiors follow their progeny to the abattoir.[30] A similar research approach is used at many experiment stations with beef cattle, dairy cattle, sheep, swine, and poultry.

BROILERS

Probably the most remarkable progress in animal breeding has been achieved with poultry. This is not surprising. Genetic improvement is the consequence of gradual progress generation by generation, and it is possible to get several generations of chickens into the record books in the same two years that it takes a single calf to grow from conception to a baby beef. Also, one hen can produce a lot more offspring for selection than a cow. Today leading producers employ their own geneticists and statisticians and they patent their private strains of birds.

As recently as 1955 a broiler chick required 3 pounds of feed to make 1 pound of gain. By 1960 there were commercial flocks that made 1 pound of gain on less than 2.5 pounds of feed. In a recent trial the University of Georgia produced a pen of eight broilers that averaged 4.28 pounds on 8 pounds of feed in eight weeks. Of course the feed is getting "hotter" and the broilers are becoming better converters with every step of progress. High-energy or "hot" feed is a mixture high in protein and high in fat, which results in rapid gain. This is important because the faster the chicks can be raised, the greater the number of flocks that can be handled in a year by given manpower and given facilities. Broiler houses are expensive. Some are three stories high. Some are 600 feet long. They house as many as 40,000 or 50,000 birds for every workman. Poultry growers, like metropolitan real estate syndicates, must secure maximum tenancy to make their accommodations profitable. To produce a 3 pound bird in twelve weeks was considered efficient a decade ago. Now a commercial flock should hit an average of 3.4 pounds in eight to nine weeks. Such a fast turnover cuts down overhead.

THE STATUS SEEKERS

Two Australian scientists, G. McBride and F. Foenander, of the University of Queensland, have come upon what may be the biological factor that limits the practical size and design of big poultry houses.[33] Despite the newest facilities for living, chickens persist in primitive habits. In the finest of modern environments barnyard social instincts prevail. Flocks insist upon establishing a pecking order by which birds of a high social status may annoy those lower than themselves if they do not show respect. Tensions reign until this chain of prestige is established in a newly assembled flock of chicks.

Researchers McBride and Foenander say an obstacle to satisfactory social stratification in enormous commercial flocks is that there are just too many birds for individual chicks with their tiny brains to remember and classify. Members of the flock become confused and frustrated not knowing just where each stands. Eventually it seems that sub-groups of chickens form neighborhoods in which the task becomes easier. If by chance a bird should wander out of its neighborhood, it gets packed back into its own group by those who do not want strangers in their midst. The Australian scientists hope, by studying the social life of poultry in mass housing, to come up with designs that will make it easier for the birds to form cliques, recognize one another, and settle down. It is possible that a by-product of their investigation may be some improvement in the design of public housing in the United States.

CHANGES IN PRODUCTION AND MARKETING— CONTRACT FARMING

A combination of better germ plasm, better feeds, and a better technology have converted broiler production into a factory industry. Even the farmer has been revamped. No longer is he likely to be his own boss, even in his own chicken houses. The risks of market fluctuations and the heavy costs of thousands of birds and their feed have made him hedge. The average broiler grower chooses to be a piece worker under contract to some feed dealer or processor who takes the risk. An efficient broiler grower makes a good income for himself and his sponsor when he can market at two cents a pound over costs of production. In an industry as competitive as the broiler business is today this is one way for the little man without everything to find some security. Rather than try to lick the processors, he can join them. Of course that means they will boss and he will say yes, even on his own farm. If this is hard, so is life. The process of integration need not end with just a single tie-up between farm and processor. It can go the full distance from field and barn to the retail chain store, and those involved can all lean on one another. Whoever puts up most of the credit will issue the orders. The system is similar to that by which the "independent" service station operator joins the oil industry. The boom in contract farming in recent years is just one more indication of the industrial nature of modern agriculture.

The small operator can get credit more easily if he has an agreement with a processor which assures him of a fixed market price. Frequently it is the processor himself who grants or guarantees the credit. In return the farmer settles in advance for a margin of profit which will save him from disaster but seldom make him rich. In effect he accepts a wage in return for a reduced risk. Since he relies chiefly on someone else's capital or credit he could hardly expect more. In return for financial support the processor gets an assured supply of raw material at a low price. If the market is demolished by overproduction the processor takes a licking. He may even be liquidated and, if he is, the whole of his empire may collapse with him. If the market zooms, the bonanza is usually split between the processor and the farmer according to some prearranged formula. As a rule the checks and balances of competition and "fair trade" keep the market from either skidding or skyrocketing, but occasionally the big wheels try to roll over one another in a price war.

Contract farming is most highly developed in those branches of agriculture where turnover is fast and operating expenses exceed the value of farm real estate. Many freezing and canning crops are produced under such arrangements but poultry production is the prime example. Georgia leads all fifty states in this industry, yet Georgians were picking cotton rather than plucking broilers twenty-five years ago. In 1935 only a half million broilers were marketed in Georgia. In 1960, 320 million were sold there.[34]

In the old cotton country of piedmont Georgia the wounds of soil erosion and human poverty are healing fast. The sharecropper has almost disappeared. Tree farms, lush pastures, and ponds of catfish define a new landscape. In many places light industry in brick-glass buildings, concrete highways, and Zebu cattle have rubbed out the clapboard shanty, red mud roads, and the mule. Here and there gaunt brick chimneys mark habitations of the past;

the houses they once warmed have been demolished, the field workers are gone. The Negroes are "chicken catching" for the broiler houses. The whites are in the new factories.

It was a bright sunny day in December of 1961 when two men drove into the Georgia piedmont. At the side of a new highway they saw a fine industrial building and a sign which proclaimed it to be a broiler processing plant. The men decided to have a look, so they parked their car and made their way inside. To their surprise, they found the machinery was shut down. In an office just off the dressing floor a supervisor in a white butcher coat sat dejectedly. He had time to talk for there was little else to do. The plant, he informed his visitors, had once rated as the largest in the world. In one twenty-four-hour day it could process three-quarters of a million pounds. It was capable of filling shipload orders for Europe on short notice. A fleet of semi-trailer trucks could deliver birds to all points of the country from the freezer plant where its production was stored. Just a year before, all the old machinery in the building had been completely removed in one operation — the way viscera is removed from a broiler. The newly installed equipment was of glistening stainless steel.

On the day when the visitors happened to arrive the plant was shut down because the bottom had fallen out of the broiler market. Chickens which had cost 15 cents a pound to grow were bringing 10 cents a pound. At such prices the processing plant, which financed farmers under contract, was losing $12,000 to $15,000 every day it worked. "If we have six more weeks like the last six we'll be finished," exclaimed the white-cloaked supervisor. "We'd be better off if we could shut down completely, but we've got millions of birds on contract farms; we have to take them when they're ready." The supervisor said the plant earns a cent a pound when it dresses a bird, so the five-cent loss on the farms was reduced to four cents by the processing plant. "We dress 9,600 birds an hour," he told the visitors. "Sometimes I stand there on the line and watch them go by — every one that weighs 3 pounds is a 12-cent loss. It's enough to drive you nuts. Our trouble is we're too small to stand this kind of pressure."

It did not make sense to the visitors that one of the largest processing plants in the world was in trouble because it was too small. Just who is big in this business, they wondered. The supervisor proceeded to explain the facts of life: "We're an independent; that's our difficulty. We're alone. We have only five feed mills and five hatcheries in our organization. We have no grain elevators at one end and no chain stores at the other. We have to take whatever the market will pay. We are not A&P or Safeway. There's a war on right now — Quaker Oats, General Mills, Ralston Purina, and a few other big grain dealers are trying to kill each other off. They're selling below cost and we're caught in the middle. We'll go broke before they will — you can believe it. They know that too. They're waiting for us to fall in their lap. They all have other lines to make up their losses. We are in broilers; that's all."

The strategy of the integrated broiler industry began to dawn on the visitors. They had walked into a processing plant to see modern technology in action and instead had received a firsthand lesson in the new economics of agriculture and the food industry. Even a processor with five feed mills and five hatcheries could find himself out on a multi-million-dollar limb if he were not hooked up with a big grain house which could underwrite the feed supplies or with a national retail chain which could dispose of vast quantities of the finished product to its millions of patrons. The rivalry can be ruthless among the giants at the top and they, too, can get hurt.

The cutthroat battle for control of the poultry industry, which in 1961 killed off thousands of farmers, scores of processors, and eliminated, at least temporarily, so powerful an empire builder as General Mills, led some business leaders to forecast that within ten years the poultry enterprise of the nation would be controlled by less than twenty-five companies. Reflecting on this prediction by the industry itself, farm editor Leland DuVall of the *Arkansas*

Gazette was constrained to write: "A vigorous agriculture is possible only because production facilities are in the hands of a great many competitive individuals. If this situation should change and if the corporation replaced the individual, consumers would have plenty of reason to complain about pressure from inflation."[35]

THE SMALL FARMER

Considering the new economic structure which prevails in some segments of agriculture, ideas about what is a small farmer are relative and bound to change. Recently Senator John J. Williams of Delaware revealed to fellow legislators that a government aid program designed to help small farmers had loaned two broiler producers a total of $3.5 million in less than eighteen months. Referring to the loan program in general the Senator remarked, "Just look at the number of loans in the $50,000, $100,000 and even $1 million class."[36] Clearly the day seemed to be at hand when it would again be an advantage to be what the Department of Agriculture calls a small farmer.

TREND

Earl F. Crouse, vice president of the Doane Agricultural Service, says that "A system of contract farming patterned after the contracts and subcontracts of industry is being forged as rapidly as knowhow and financing can be brought together." This prominent farm consultant warns that "the transition will be painful" but adds that when it is complete farmers will have attained economic equality by becoming full-fledged and equal members of our industrial economy.[37] He does not estimate how many little operators will lose control of their farms while going through the meatgrinder.

Contract farming is already underway in pork, beef, and milk production. Arthur B. Maurer, a packer of Kansas City, Missouri, has said it "is the beginning of a revolution in swine raising." Packer Maurer claims that by working with corporations in such integrated operations farmers are assured of a market. In his opinion "individualism has outlived its usefulness in agriculture."[38]

A recent study of who controls what in the food processing industries reveals that considerable concentration has already taken place in that branch of the economy. Consolidation at the farm level is only following a pattern which has been set farther up the line. As the two segments of production and processing are linked to the big distributing chains the integration will be complete. The study of the processors showed that out of 2,646 meat packers four controlled 34 per cent of the business. Out of 5,008 fluid milk dairies the four largest handled 23 per cent of all sales. There were 34 makers of breakfast foods, but the top four had 83 per cent of the market. There were 1,347 canners of fruits and vegetables but four leading firms did 29 per cent of the business.[39]

A SENSE OF VALUE

Albert Kner, director of the design laboratory of the Container Corporation of America, has an explanation for this trend toward market control by a few top processors. It is consumer preference. Designer Kner is convinced that a food package is a status symbol and not just a wrapper. "The customer," Mr. Kner recently informed a grocery study group, "will turn increasingly to those packages that make him feel he can acquire added 'status' by using or serving the product offered . . ."[40] Farmers may have marveled that housewives are willing to pay so much for fancy packaging. Now they know that the "socially conscious" housewife may be more concerned about displaying the outside of a package than she is with serving what is inside.

R. J. Hug, president of the General Baking Company, announced not long ago that competition from private labels looms as the biggest "headache" in the bread baking industry.[41] The American Bakers Association clings to a more old-fashioned theme and declares that the farmers' price-supported wheat is responsible for the high cost of bread. When the National City Bank looked

into the bread tragedy it came up with some figures of interest to
the quantitative analyst. It found that a loaf of bread selling for
20.3 cents represents 2.8 cents worth of wheat and other farm products, 5.5 cents worth of baking and wrapping, 9.1 cents worth of
selling and delivery, and 2.9 cents worth of milling, taxes, and miscellaneous.[41] It is the same story with milk. Farmers who get 8 to
12 cents a quart for milk which sells for from 20 to 30 cents a quart
have long wondered why it is that beer and colas made in push-
button factories retail for more than their product which requires
so much effort by man and cow. Dairymen complain that the de-
livery-salesman who peddles door to door and has no capital of his
own invested in the business makes more per quart than they do.
Integration on that basis is not particularly appealing.

CO-OPS

The Farm Bureau objects to contract farming. It is convinced
that under such arrangements the farmer loses his "traditional in-
dividuality."[38] The Bureau contends that farmers should integrate
themselves by organizing farmer-controlled cooperatives with the
assistance of the Farm Bureau. The co-op is organized agriculture's
most effective economic weapon, especially when it is used on the
offense rather than on the defense. Agricultural cooperatives are
used offensively when their members are able to keep production
in approximate balance with market demand. Cooperatives which
have sufficient control over the total market supply of the commodities they handle allocate production quotas among their members to prevent surpluses. They set quality standards and also act
as the sole marketing agent for members. With such discipline it
it easier to bargain for agreeable profit margins.

The most successful co-ops are those which have seized the offensive. Cooperative arrangements in citrus fruits, raisins, and
cranberries have been remarkably successful. By strict quality control and uniform grading the co-ops have been able to win and
keep the patronage of major food jobbers and retail outlets. In this

era of intensive competition for mass markets uniformity of quality and grade is essential to retailers, particularly the mammoth chains. A customer should find the same quality under the same label whether the item is bought in Hawaii, Alaska, or Virginia. A co-op, or a group of co-ops, under good management can guarantee this kind of uniformity. The chains and other responsible retailers will pay a premium for precise quantities of specified grades which are attractively and uniformly packed. The discipline necessary to produce a standardized output must begin at the farm, and thus it is that the co-ops often act as filters, admitting to membership or to favorable quota status only those farmers who can comply with rigid specifications. The struggle for survival or supremacy within the successful co-ops is one of the most cutthroat in agri-business. Farmers with high quotas in skillfully managed co-ops are among the elite of American agriculture, for they have a solid piece of a prime market.

A majority of co-ops, however, serve farmers who specialize in crops which are in surplus supply. These co-ops are on the defensive and their usefulness to members is somewhat limited. Most wheat and dairy co-ops are in this category. Where there is no effective internal control over production there can be no external control over the market price. Obviously to operate advantageously a cooperative must include a majority of producers and it must limit the production of members to that amount which can be sold at a profitable price. This is what the U. S. Department of Agriculture calls "supply management." The Department hopes that through cooperative supply management farmers eventually will gain enough bargaining power to negotiate for higher prices directly in the market place — a development which would take the pressure off the federal budget for farm subsidies. The object is to shift the cost of crop price support from the taxpayer to the food consumer. While the two are practically synonymous it has been said by some astute critics of price support policy that the cost will not be so noticeable to the public under supply management.[42] However, Professor Hendrik S. Houthakker has noted that "Supply Management, in fact, is merely a euphemism for 'Monopoly.' "[42]

In recent years, as the total farm population has declined, the power of the cooperatives has grown. A further drop in the numbers of farms is certain to improve the position of the co-ops. In 1940, when there were 6.3 million farms, cooperatives marketed 20 per cent of all produce sold. Two decades later in 1960, when there were 3.7 million farms, cooperatives handled 28 per cent of all marketings.[43-44] A 40 per cent drop in the number of farms was accompanied by a 40 per cent increase in the proportion of sales marketed through cooperatives. The trends are related. Although it may seem incongruous that a farm organization should grow stronger as the number of farmers declines, the explanation is simple. The effectiveness of co-ops, just like the effectiveness of other vertically integrated entrepreneurial enterprises, increases as weaklings drop out and the stronger survivors set about to build more efficient organizations. It takes farmers who are financially strong and well versed in economics to check production voluntarily in order to establish a favorable position for collective bargaining. The technique is the same as that used by industry, organized labor, and professional societies such as the American Medical Association. The poor and unsophisticated cannot play this game; they are too numerous, they lack credit, and they lack perception. It is the ability of the co-op, when on the offensive, to carry out supply management and secure higher returns for less production that is its greatest potential asset. In 1940 marketing cooperatives disposed of $1.7 billion in farm produce. By 1960, the total had grown to $9.5 billion.[43]

As the number of farms shrinks and the co-ops grow stronger the biggest power play in American agriculture begins to shape up between the co-ops on one side and the chain stores on the other. Both are vertically integrated and thus benefit from the efficiencies of the agri-business system. Both can employ the best professional management. Both have their sights set on the consumer, for everybody knows that the one certain way to raise profits is to win consumer preference. At this time, however, neither is in a position to make an all-out effort to dominate the other. Rather, they are plagued by the eagerness of too many farmers to produce to a maximum, and by the bitter rivalry among the chains. Overproduction depresses prices at the farm and wrecks the bargaining position of the defensive co-ops. Rivalry between the chains results in low markups. Thus, while competition continues the consumer is the beneficiary and the net result is cheap food. The low cost of food is due as much to cutthroat competition among the chains as it is to the technological revolution in agriculture.

The hope of top co-op management is that the number of undisciplined overproducers will decline to a point where better organized co-op farmers who are coached in supply management will be able to switch to the offensive and establish a more stable and profitable level of production for the major crops. The success of a few co-ops dealing in minor crops gives substance to this hope. When a farm editor recently urged his readers to affiliate with marketing cooperatives he indicated that "Bargaining power puts you in a position to control — or partially control — prices and other conditions for a sale. Sellers have a natural advantage, or bargaining power, when supplies fall short of the real demand."[45] Another farm magazine reported that "Improved bargaining power for farmers has been accepted as an important policy objective by most major farm organizations . . . Once there is collective action, the organized group can work to increase demand, reduce supply, or improve marketing. Inelastic demand makes reducing supply look attractive to many groups. For example, the 1960 farm value of hogs was $2.9 billion. With fewer hogs in 1958, the farm value was a half billion higher — $3.4 billion."[46]

THE CONSUMER

Faced with the threat of supply management the consumer need not abandon all hope. It is, after all, his appetite which everyone strives to appease. If he did not consume, then all the bright ambitions of commerce would fade into darkness. But there may be physical limits to what the consumer can eat or his purse afford. Supply management which ignores these critical limits is doomed. This the ice cream dispensers of New York's Upper Broadway recently discovered to their humiliation. During a mid-August hot spell these resourceful entrepreneurs collectively agreed on a new system of catering. They resolved that customers would have to buy two scoops of ice cream at a time; the less profitable one-scoop-at-a-time was out. Children on restricted budgets pleaded but the frosty hearts of the monopolists did not melt. However, the vendors had not reckoned with His Honor, the Mayor of New York, a man who knows the full rewarding satisfaction of a single scoop of ice cream, and who can always be reached directly via Post Office Box 100 when there is a civic crisis.

Into that special box there was delivered one day a plaintive letter from a dean at Columbia University. The dean had heard of the children's plight and verified it. He, like they, had been refused a single dip and what did the Mayor think of that? At City Hall they say the Mayor turned to his Commissioner of Markets and the Commissioner of Markets paid a friendly visit to the ice cream emporia on Upper Broadway where it was decided that supply management was all a mistake. It seems that the Mayor, after cogitating on children and ice cream, had observed, "It seems to me that anyone who wants a single scoop of ice cream should be able to get it."[47]

EFFICIENCY

As all segments of American agriculture have amply demonstrated, the surest way to prosper is not through artificially rigged bargaining power but through increased efficiency. When farmers integrate with processors, or when co-ops provide a medium for collective bargaining, the efficient producer ultimately reaps more benefit than the inefficient producer. A contract price which is favorable to the average producer will prove a balloon to the efficient and a sinker to the incompetent or undercapitalized. Efficiency on a mass scale is more profitable than efficiency on a small scale. Thus a good manager must have ample capital if he is to use his talents to their full extent. A good manager without capital is handicapped. It goes without saying that capital in the hands of an incompetent is wasted.

The recent course of evolution in the dairy industry confirms this general conclusion. What is particularly significant about dairying is the rapidity with which new adjustments are taking place. No major segment of American agriculture is now undergoing a more profound and accelerated shakedown. In 1950 there were 3.6 million farms with milk cows. By 1959 there were only 1.8 million.[48] Nevertheless, depressed as the general market for dairy products appears to be, there are conditions under which it provides an incentive to those with capital to expand their operations. In 1950 there were 3,593 dairy farms in the United States with more than 100 cows. By 1959 the number of farms with over 100 cows had risen to 6,594, and there were at least 34 farms with over 1,000 milk cows each.[48]

DREAM WORLD

The tourist in southern Florida finds rich fare in a trip around the rim of Lake Okeechobee if he is fascinated by the wild swamps of the Everglades and the engineering techniques of modern reclamation. He sees landscapes of native flora that have changed little since the days of Spanish exploration. Almost alongside he observes some of the most advanced drainage and irrigation projects to be found anywhere. This is one of the nation's most prosperous winter farming districts, specializing in sugar cane, fresh vegetables, and intensive dairying. As the resort cities of Florida's coasts have boomed in population the inland rural districts have prospered.

North of the town of Okeechobee, where the flat landscape is accented by the feather-duster plumes of palm trees, the traveler comes suddenly upon the tidy, white-fenced domain of the Mc-Arthur Dairy. A sign tells him that he is welcome to enter. Thus he has an invitation to see for himself a 20th century bovine dream world unmatched for its scale anywhere in America. In 1928 the McArthur Dairy began operations with 20 cows in open country that was eventually to become part of Miami: 1928 is almost "ancient times" as the history of southern Florida is recounted. In subsequent years more people came into the area and built. Miami grew and the little dairy was forced to move farther into the country. It made several moves of this sort, retreating before the advance of the city only to be caught again. With each shift the market improved and the herd increased. By 1962 the enterprise had grown to 8,000 registered Jerseys — enough to stock 400 average Wisconsin dairy farms.

By 1962 the McArthur Dairy had transferred most of its operations to the wilderness north of Lake Okeechobee. There it had turned thousands of acres of wild land into productive year-round pastures sufficient to accommodate most of its herd. Plans have been made to consolidate the entire enterprise at Okeechobee. Already four giant milking barns have been constructed. These white barns are immaculate and each cow is given a scrubdown shower under a hose before milking. The milk itself goes directly from the milking machines to stainless steel refrigeration tanks. A fleet of refrigerated trucks hauls the milk to bottling plants. There are three small villages, each of about thirty houses, for the families of herdsmen and milkers. The homes for the workmen are new and the villages have palm-lined streets. Buses shuttle children to and from the public schools.

Eventually when all 8,000 Jerseys are assembled at Okeechobee there will be seven milking barns and around 150 families of permanent help. Construction is already underway. A number of the present milkers and herdsmen are former dairy farmers who sold their own properties to become a part of the McArthur team. Cows are milked on a round-the-clock schedule. The men work in shifts and the cows follow an equally precise routine which divides their life between pasture and barn. Not only is the scale of operations impressive but the orderliness and cleanliness of the whole establishment leaves the visitor with the conviction that milk could not be produced under more favorable conditions. It is an operation that could set the pace for the future dairy industry granted enough markets like that in southern Florida. There are farms similar to it in almost every state with a large urban population; they vary primarily in scale and in certain techniques that are appropriate to particular climates.

THE OTHER HALF

Today financial distress among smaller dairy farmers is as aggravated as it is among small cotton growers. In 1960 all the nation's dairymen produced 122 billion pounds of milk, but less than half, 58 billion pounds, had a ready consumer market as bottle milk. The balance was processed into butter, cheese, and other products for which there is inadequate demand. Because of the difference in demand, consumers' bottled milk has a wholesale value at the farm that is around 50 per cent greater than processors' milk, although generally there is little difference in quality or costs of production. Often the two are really only one and the classification is made by a bookkeeper. Both kinds of milk can come from the same cow and go to the same dairy via the same tank truck without the farmer knowing what is going to happen to it. Later he is paid a "blended" price depending on how much the co-op sells as bottling milk and how much it sells for processing. In 1960 surplus processors' milk averaged $3.39 per hundredweight at the farm. Consumers' bottling milk averaged $5.48 per hundredweight.

Looking at the picture nationwide, almost one-third of all milk produced in 1959 came from 8 per cent of the dairy farms. At the opposite end of the scale 43 per cent of the dairymen produced only 13 per cent of the milk.[49] Clearly the process of elimination, once so spectacular among southern cotton growers, has hit the dairy industry for some very logical reasons. (Table 3.)

TWIN HEIFERS

A Wisconsin cow, in the heart of America's Dairyland, might have twin heifer calves. Should her master decide to keep one and sell the other to a farmer in Rhode Island, the day would come when both calves would be cows and their milk would go to market. While their milk would be identical, that from the Rhode Island cow would be worth half again as much as the milk from her sister who remained in Wisconsin. That is because Rhode Island is a milk deficit state while Wisconsin produces surpluses. Practically all Rhode Island milk is put into bottles for consumption at premium prices. The bulk of Wisconsin milk is processed into cheese, butter, and other products that sell at depressed prices. The twin heifers symbolize the split personality of the modern dairy industry. (Map 1.)

SPECIALIZATION

All in all specialization and concentration are the principal trends throughout the economic structure of American agriculture. Only a comparative few out of many are able to cope with the financial and technical demands of modern farming. Lack of skill in bookkeeping and cost analysis can hurt a farmer today as much as a deficiency in the art of husbandry. The technology of management takes precedence over field or animal husbandry. A successful rancher with outfits in Montana and Wyoming came into his profession after having been vice-president of a transcontinental trucking company. Said he, as he sat comfortably in his living room before an exquisite picture-window view of the Big Horn Mountains: "If my cattle needed help in an emergency, I'd be the least useful person on this ranch. I employ a foreman for that." He had gone into ranching rather than into apartment investments in Los Angeles, he said, "First because I like country life better than

city life. Secondly, I made a cost analysis just as I did before I went
into the trucking business. I decided I could do better than the
average." Any farmer today who cannot do better than the average
is on his way out. Others are ready to replace him.

IMPACT

The technological revolution in agriculture has been more than
a switch to new machines, better germ plasm, streamlined marketing systems, and more efficient management of capital. It has affected people more than it has affected the land, yet the influence
upon the land has also been profound. Economic and social disloca-
tions in rural areas have been harder to cope with than the new
technology itself. While there are half as many people on the soil
as there were twenty-five years ago farmers are still a surplus commodity. The machine has been welcomed. Men without capital
have been rejected. Less thought has been given to the problem of
surplus men than to that of surplus crops. More anxiety has been
expressed over price supports for milk than over how to get those
surpluses consumed by people who need milk but cannot afford it.
Abuses of acreage allotment privileges and scandalous grain storage operations have aroused public indignation, but the plight of
disrupted lives has been accepted apathetically.

The way the farm problem has been dealt with resembles the
way in which urban renewal has been tackled. Depreciated physical assets have been researched with the most scrupulous attention
and generous subsidies have been granted to rehabilitate property
. . . The human problem has been swept under the rug. Surplus
farmers continue to leave the occupation which once offered Americans the best opportunity to become "self-made." Now a man
must "have it made" before he can farm. To get a better picture
of agriculture in the midst of its technological revolution, it would
be well to take a look at the variety of people who are still called
"the farmer."

Chapter 2

Who Is the
American Farmer?

As we have seen, American farmers are not one species but many. They may be anything from a weekend hobbyist in Bermuda shorts who raises strawberries for the gang at the office to a corporation with a million acres of land woven by teletype into a transcontinental empire. It would not require a detailed acquaintance with either farming or human nature to conclude that what is a favorable economic-political climate for one extreme of the agricultural spectrum might not appeal to the other. The public image of American farmers has been distorted by ambiguous language. A tendency to discuss them as though they were single rather than plural throws the public into confusion and the experts into controversy.

COUNTING THOSE WHO DO NOT COUNT

Persons are counted as farmers in the Census of Agriculture who, if the term had literal meaning rather than political connotations, would not be counted because they are of no account as husbandmen. As a group the operator families on 1.6 million "farms" —44 per cent of those listed as "farmers" in the last Census of

Agriculture — averaged only $217 net annual income from "agriculture." However, they averaged $2,884, or thirteen times more, from other sources.[1]

These 1.6 million farm families who are 7 per cent in agriculture and 93 per cent out of it were included in the census because they fall into that catch-all category which markets produce worth "more than $50 and less than $2,500 a year." Of course $50 is trivial and anything even remotely approximating that sum should not qualify a man or his property for entry in the Census of Agriculture. At first glance it might appear that $2,500 is a reasonable amount of money until it is realized that the net return to a farm operator is normally only about one-third of his gross income.[2] When that fact is considered, $2,500 gross income becomes about $800 net, and that is not enough to make a man a farmer. It is next to impossible for an American family to subsist on an annual cash income of $800 or less. To people in this category agriculture is at best a sideline or a part-time occupation. These people should not be seriously considered when farm policy is debated and formulated. Their number is very large but their production is insignificant. If all of it were eliminated this country would still have surpluses. When these fringe people or their production and "farm" incomes are averaged into summary statements about agriculture they distort the picture.

Richard E. Albrecht, editor of *Wallaces Farmer,* made this clear to his readers some time ago. Said this spokesman for rural Iowa, "We had 3,700,000 farms in 1959, but only a few over 2 million . . . farms produced about 95 per cent of the farm products sold. Remember this when looking at 'average farm' statistics. They can be misleading if part-time, retirement, and residential farms are averaged in with full time cornbelt operations."[3] If children's lemonade stands were included in a census of retail food outlets the whole grocery business might look so sick that even A&P would qualify for government aid on the basis of averaged trade data. A lot of tear-jerking about the "poor farmer" stems from treating facsimiles as though they were the genuine article.

The proposal that 1.6 million farms be eliminated from the official family of 3.7 million is not a heartless suggestion that the government and the public ignore distressed people. It is a suggestion that this bottom element in American husbandry be dismissed from consideration as farmers and that they be dealt with for what they are if they need help. Many operators in this group are retired, part-time, or hobby cultivators who are not at all in need of government assistance. The hardships that some of the remainder face cannot be attributed to the state of the nation's agriculture. If anything, they are due to the fact that these people are not really in agriculture. They are sitting on the sidelines out of the game. For the present the 1.6 million farm families most of whom derive a negligible part of their income from farming will be referred to as the "Third Class" of American agriculture. (Table 1.)

THE DESTITUTE

Within the great Third Class block of 1.6 million pseudo farmers there is a sizable minority group of 350,000 families which is truly one of the most impoverished in America.[1] In this group, which operates 9 per cent of all census farms, are many families who live more wretchedly than if they were in cities on welfare. Their annual net cash returns from sales of farm products average $438 and their off-farm earnings average $525. If all American farm families lived and worked at this low level the nation would not be as well fed as China. If all census farmers were in the same bracket with these 350,000 families the total agricultural production of the United States would be one-sixth of what it is now and famine would be universal. These people need help and they need it badly but they cannot expect to become genuine farmers because that would require capital which they do not have and cannot get.

Their future is not in agriculture but in occupations where someone else can supply the capital necessary to create decent jobs.
These people do not need a federal agricultural program. They
need a program that will stimulate industry and industrial employment.

A recent study of eight types of farms from coast to coast[5] indicates that to net $2,500 from agriculture a farmer must sell any-
where from $9,275 worth of milk as a Minnesota dairyman to
$26,454 worth of cotton and wheat as a grower of cash crops in
Oklahoma. This return, of course, does not include investment income or capital appreciation on land. Capital requirements for
farms that can produce this small amount of net labor income
range from $42,231 in the case of the Minnesota farm to $115,864
in the case of the Oklahoma unit. By contemporary commercial
standards these are small farms — the kind that is on an income
borderline and needs to become bigger or more efficient to survive.
Obviously families who clear $800 a year by "farming" cannot
hope to climb even into the $2,500 bracket.

The vast outlay of capital required to enable a man to earn $2,500
from his own labor as a farmer is one of the basic facts of modern
agriculture which is not widely acknowledged. (Tables 1 and 13.)
If it were, it would be hard to get the average city dweller to pay
taxes to help those who have so much money invested in real estate. Because labor income is so low in agriculture, the difference
between farmers who are poor and those who are well off is due
chiefly to their capital resources and therefore to the amounts of
income which they derive from capital invested. (Tables 10, 13.)
Annual federal doles in the form of crop subsidies can keep weak
undercapitalized units limping along, but they do not and never
will remedy the basic illness, which is a poor resource base.
Changes in farm technology have caught many people short of
adequate investments. Today it takes real wealth to be a successful
farmer. This is not the Jeffersonian image of the family farmer but
we live with facts, not a myth.

Since the capital requirements of agriculture are going up rather than down as the technological revolution progresses, it is no wonder that fewer and fewer persons can afford to stay in farming as full-time professional operators. While the old style "labor" farmers have been going out of business, new types of "investment" farmers and "tax-shelter" farmers have been coming in with enough funds to establish efficient units. Not only are the technology and economics of agriculture changing but so is the type of person who makes a farmer. The tax rules of the Treasury Department are having considerable influence on this evolution of modern agriculture. On the other hand people without capital to develop their land to a higher potential, yet who cling to the soil "because we don't know what else to do," are some of the most distressed human beings in America. They are trapped. They know it. They fail to see any alternative. They are beyond any real help by the Department of Agriculture although the public is under the impression that the national agricultural program can remedy their situation. It cannot.

THE OPPOSITE EXTREME

At the very pinnacle of the agricultural pyramid are 1,200 farms, each of which markets over a half million dollars worth of produce annually. (Table 1.) These 1,200 elite, which are an infinitesimal one-thirtieth of one per cent of all American farms, produce almost as much as the bottom 1.6 million census "farms" which are 44 per cent of the total. The 1,200 elite made aggregate sales of $1.4 billion out of a national total of $30.6 billion in the last census year. The 1.6 million "farmers" in the Third Class sold $1.6 billion worth of crops and livestock. In short it took the produce of 1,000 average "farmers" at the bottom to equal the sales of 1 genuine farmer at the top.

Just 102,000 farms constitute the leading 3 per cent of American agriculture. Each of these units sells more than $40,000 worth of produce annually. Within this group are the 1,200 elite which market more than half a million dollars worth of commodities apiece. There are also 21,000 "junior elite" with sales of more than $100,000 but less than $500,000. The remaining 80,000 "blue ribbon" farms sell between $40,000 and $100,000 worth of crops and livestock annually. Aggregate sales by the combined 3 per cent at the top reached $9.65 billion in the last census year. This was 31.5 per cent of the value of all marketings by American farms. (Table 1.) If the United States had 300,000 instead of 102,000 farms like these it could dispense with all the remainder. In other words if only 9 per cent of the nation's farms were as productive as the top 3 per cent there would be no need for crops from the other 91 per cent. As it is, *the top 3 per cent produce more than the bottom 78 per cent.*

It is the amazing productivity at the very top of American agriculture which sets the sizzling pace for all the remainder. Unless the magnitude and intensity of this competition is grasped it is impossible to understand why the majority of farmers are in trouble. Quite understandably the operators of big farms live more on their investment and entrepreneurial incomes than on their labor incomes. It is not the physical work they do which counts but rather how well they manage their capital. (Tables 10, 13.) Big agriculture is big business and it takes the best connections in the market, in finance, and in politics to get to the top. No man can afford to fly blind at such an altitude; he must know precisely how he rates or he may crash disastrously. As one big-time entrepreneur in California remarked when he lured a university professor onto his farm payroll at $20,000 a year, "He may not be worth that as a scientist, but he knows his way around." The Commercial Solvents Corporation of New York, which financed Texas cotton planter Billie Sol Estes in some of his operations, judiciously put a former Under Secretary of Agriculture on its payroll to check out "general policies . . ." in Washington before making vital moves.[6]

The top 3 per cent of American agriculture is flanked by another

210,000 able producers who market annually between $20,000 and $40,000 worth of commodities. The output of this group, which contains 6 per cent of all census farmers, is 20 per cent of the national total. If we were to combine all the producers in the various upper brackets who make sales of $20,000 or more we would have what might be called America's "First Class of Husbandry." Those in the First Class are 8.3 per cent of all census farmers and ranchers but they account for 50 per cent of all output.

Faced with this kind of competition any medium-sized operators who want to continue as full-time professionals must change their style and go all-out for growth and maximum production. Either that or call in the government as referee and arrange a truce by which the market is divided among present producers before it is too late. By and large the big and growing segments of agriculture are anti government interference. They are after all the market they can get while the getting is good. Many of the smaller producers are getting scared. Quite a few have unfurled the white flag for protection.

THE UPPER MIDDLE CLASS

Between the numerous but inconsequential Third Class which raises 5 per cent of the nation's food and the rather narrow but immensely productive First Class, there lies a sizable Middle Class of 1.8 million. But this Middle Class, which sells 45 per cent of all farm goods, is by no means homogeneous. It is the Upper Middle Class of 483,000 which corresponds better than any other group to that cornfed stereotype of the family homestead surrounded by green fields and fat hogs, presided over by a jolly man in a straw hat and overalls. The 483,000 Upper Middle Class farms are 13 per cent of the census total and they account for 22 per cent of all crops and livestock. Farm owners in this category are comparatively prosperous, for they market commodities worth $10,000 to $20,000 annually. (Table 1.) They are not rich but they are substantial.

Nevertheless, only 36 per cent of the Upper Middle Class are full owners; 37 per cent are part-owners;[7] while 27 per cent are tenants (Table 9).

The degree of tenancy among the Upper Middle Class is about 35 per cent above the average for all census farms, which is 20 per cent. Tenancy is 23 per cent on farms in the First Class, as Table 9 shows. The weaker ownership status of operators on better farms as compared with operators on poorer farms indicates how difficult it is to get the capital necessary for the big operations. Thirty-four per cent of all farms purchased in 1960 were bought by persons who were not farmers.[8] As a rule, however, a tenant operator on a relatively good farm earns a higher income than an owner-operator on an inferior unit. Also, because tenants must furnish some or all machinery and livestock, it may require more capital to be a tenant on a farm in the Upper Middle Class than to be an owner in the Lower Middle Class.

THE LOWER MIDDLE CLASS

The big Lower Middle Class is next in line for serious attrition. There are 1.3 million units in this category which produces from $2,500 to $10,000 worth of commodities annually (Table 1). Since net incomes average about one-third of sales,[9] the operators of these farms have labor incomes of perhaps between $800 and $3,300 annually. Their average net income from farming was $1,740 in the last census year. Their average earnings outside of agriculture were $1,816.[1] This indicates that as a group they are already more than halfway out of farming into other employment. Perhaps it will not be more than another generation before most of the 1.3 million Lower Middle Class farmers join the 1.6 million in Third Class.

The Lower Middle Class will fade partially for lack of recruits. Young people do not want a life based on a net annual labor income of $800 to $3,300. Nearly two-thirds (64.7 per cent) of the properties in this category are operated by persons 45 years of age or older. As a rule these older people do not want to leave the land although they are willing to take on town jobs if they can commute.* Many of these operators started farming in the age of horse agriculture. They are leftovers from another era. It is not the sort of business that attracts people of modest means who have hopes for the future. As one newlywed couple in Arkansas remarked, "We had a chance to travel before we were married. We found out there is inside plumbing, spin-dry washers, and outboard motor boats. Dad wants to give us his farm if we'll run it but we prefer to be city people. We're staying in town where we both have jobs. We go out to see him on Sundays and sometimes we fish in his pond."

On farms that yield so little income the bare necessities of life consume all that the operators can earn; there is little opportunity to save for modernization or expansion. The chances are that not more than half of the farms in the Lower Middle Class will ever get over the hump into the Upper Middle Class. In the days of horse agriculture things were different. To get ahead a young couple raised a big family and as the children grew up they raised an extra team of horses, cleared more land, and let the boys do a man's work. Today it is not necessarily an advantage to have many children on a farm and it takes capital to buy a second tractor together with proper hydraulic attachments. Then, too, the kind of equipment used on small farms does not make the most efficient use of manpower.

On some elite properties in the First Class there are huge diesel tractors with four-bottom two-way plows which run day and night. When weather conditions are right and large areas must be covered, costly equipment should be available and ready to operate around the clock. You see the gleam of the headlights on the ma-

---

* The Bureau of the Census reports that in 1960 of all persons on farms between 25 and 64 years of age 10 per cent were between 25 and 29; 11 per cent were 30 to 34; 28 per cent were 35 to 44; and 51 per cent were 45 to 65. There were more persons over 65 than in the 25–34 bracket.

chines after dusk and before dawn, while during daylight hours they are shrouded in clouds of dust of their own making. They are the Douglas DC–8's of agriculture and so efficient that an operator who has enough land cannot afford to be without them. The tractor sells for $32,000, the plow for $7,000. The combination of these two standard implements costs more than most farms in the Lower Middle Class would cost if all their livestock and small-size machinery were included. The value of all the land and buildings of the average farm in the Lower Middle Class is $27,451, whereas these assets on the average farm in First Class are worth $135,070. (Table 13.)

Young people today, as in times past, will put up with privation if they see a future in it, but if their credit is not good for a capital loan which will enable them to reach a higher plateau of farm operation, they smartly avoid the trap entirely. The property they might have inherited, if they wanted to work on it, goes into the soil bank or is sold to a wealthier operator to expand his enterprise.

THE FUTURE

Out of this quick survey of farm stratification a few questions seem to emerge. For example, which brackets are growing and into which brackets is production being concentrated? The figures brought together in Table 2 give the picture. Farms in the First and Upper Middle Classes grew substantially during the decade of the 1950's. Their combined numbers rose from 484,000 to 794,000 and as a result they became 21.5 per cent of all farms in 1959 instead of 9.0 per cent in 1950. These classes enhanced their position in the market place even faster. While advancing 12.5 per cent in their share of all farms they advanced their share of agricultural sales from 51 per cent of the total in 1950 to 72 per cent in 1959 — a handsome gain of 21 per cent.

Third Class "farms" accounted for most of the census casualties, for their numbers declined from 3.3 million in 1950 to 1.6 million in 1959. A change in census definition of farms accounted for about

0.2 million of this loss. As the proportion of farms in Third Class dropped from 61 per cent of all in 1950 to 44 per cent in 1959 their proportion of the market declined from 12 per cent to 5 per cent. While this group had a real loss in numbers of about 50 per cent it lost 57 per cent of its former position in sales.

More important than what happened to the fringe farmers in Third Class is the deteriorating status of operators in the Lower Middle Class. While this group had a net decline in numbers from 1.6 million in 1950 to 1.27 million in 1959, it had a slight relative growth from 30 per cent of all farms in 1950 to 34 per cent in 1959. The most significant development, as far as this very large number of operators is concerned, is that their relative position in the total production picture deteriorated badly during the 1950's. While they accounted for 37 per cent of all produce sold in 1950, they made only 23 per cent of the sales in 1959. It is this severe relative loss of position with respect to agriculture's total production and sales which spells crisis for the Lower Middle Class.

Whether the taxpaying consumer will continue to approve of expensive government aid to the distressed segment of agriculture is another question that arises. It has become all too apparent in recent years that most federal help does not really reach those who need it most. The taxpayer is growing critical. He will have to be shown that his subsidies do not either featherbed incompetence or serve as an unnecessary bonus to the efficient. If he judges by the past the taxpayer may conclude that the sooner the government gets out of agriculture the better. If he does, the efficient farmers will find an alternative. The weak will have an even rougher time. The rapid trend toward the concentration of agricultural production on a relatively small number of farms in the First and Upper Middle Classes (Table 2) was one of the most significant developments in the 1950's.

On the complex subject of taxes, federal farm programs and the squeeze on the middle class farmer, Representative Harlan Hagen of California had a few words to say before the House in September of 1962.[10] Said Congressman Hagen: "Mr. Speaker, those of us who attempt to take an objective look at the farm problem in the interest of our farmer constituents and the taxpayer and the consumer are quite disturbed over the fixation which evidently prevails at policy levels of the Department of Agriculture with the idea that the only rational solution to the farm problem for almost all commodities is an incentive level of price support with the multiplication of controls, [allotments] which such a program requires. . . . These programs guarantee uneconomic production by a class of distress farmers and make millionaires at the corporate farming end of the farm community to the detriment of the middle-class farmers who are squeezed by quotas into uneconomic production activities by the product of the pigmies and the giants." Representative Hagen concluded his remarks with the following observation: "The fact is that our farm programs should be primarily directed at the welfare of these same middle-class farmers who are the custodians of the farm values, both economic and sociological, of which we boast. Unfortunately, concern for them has not been the primary concern of past farm programs."

SURVIVAL OF THE FITTEST

Up until 1951 potatoes were grown under government acreage allotments. A majority of producers voted for these controls in order to get the federal price supports which went with them. As it worked out, however, the growers defeated their own ends by being too efficient. Year after year the government, in an effort to bring supply down to within range of demand, cut back its acreage allotments, but the eager farmers regularly outsmarted the statisticians by planting better seed stock, applying more fertilizer, and getting bigger harvests. These were the days when the government bought potatoes every winter for several dollars a barrel, dyed them purple, and sold them to starch factories for a few cents a barrel. The farmers were happy but the city taxpayer fumed because he paid a high price for what he ate and extra taxes for the waste. A taxpayers' rebellion forced the government to order a drastic cut in allotments. This the farmer refused to accept, so price supports were withdrawn and growers were left to plant as much as they pleased for whatever prices they could get. Subsequent developments provide a good example of how the rule of the "survival of the fittest" takes over when federal impediments to competition are removed. It is also an illustration of the intensity of contemporary specialization in agriculture.

Aroostook County in Maine leads all other counties of the United States in potato production but in 1962 it experienced a depression. In April of that year potatoes sold for as little as 62 cents a barrel although it cost over $2.00 a barrel to produce them. The market price had been above $3.00 a barrel during the previous winter but many growers kept their crops snug in earth-mounded storehouses waiting for even higher prices. When the market broke, hopes for a killing turned to despair. Just about every year since 1953 there has been overproduction. Sometimes the market paid a profit; sometimes it did not, and a lot of growers were wiped out.

It was in May of 1962 that Paul Rhone, a spare man in his middle years with a swarthy complexion and thinning black hair, looked out of a window across the rolling hills of the St. Johns Valley near Ft. Kent in Aroostook County. This was the tenth season that Mr. Rhone had stayed out of his own fields while he watched some of his neighbors disk their stony brown soils in preparation for planting. "Each year there are fewer of them," he remarked. "It won't be long before these will quit. They are in debt for all they're worth. Even their crops are mortgaged before they're planted. In 1950 there were eighty-seven farmers in our town. Last year there were twenty-one. Now I just found out that three more won't plant this year. I must have been inspired to quit when I did in 1953. I still have my farm without a lien on it. I'm in the soil bank and I'm going to stay there until 1969. By that time I'll be fifty-eight. Let's face it: that's too old to resume farming again so one of these days I'll plant all the fields to trees. I want to leave something of value to my son."

One could tell that Paul Rhone, formerly a Lower Middle Class operator, was a reluctant drop-out, but he could not help congratulating himself upon quitting when he did. He had salvaged something, which is more than some of the die-hards were able to do. He continued to reminisce: "My grandfather cleared this land of woods. My father picked up the big stones and made a nice farm of it. Now I'll put it back to trees again — three generations from woods to woods. All a little hundred-and-sixty-acre farm like mine was ever good for was potatoes. Now it's not good for that. We planted between twenty-five and fifty acres, depending on the times, and kept a few sheep. Today we'd have to plant twice as much and then maybe we'd lose. It's a nice place to live and I enjoy it, but I rely on my job in town. I'm lucky because I dropped out early. Now there aren't enough jobs to go around in Ft. Kent. Men my age who farmed all their lives have gone to Pratt-Whitney in Hartford, Connecticut. Some have left their families here. Others have taken them down there; they spend all they make to live in three-decker tenements. The young people of Ft. Kent leave for Hartford as soon as they are grown-up. They get jobs easily because Acadians have a reputation for being good workers. But it's a lonesome life. There are so many Acadians down in the Connecticut Valley they've organized a French club in Hartford. I guess every Newberry's dime store in Southern New England has Ft. Kent girls behind the counters."

When Paul Rhone was asked if the survivors were the best farmers he replied, "I wouldn't say that. Maybe some of the smart ones dropped out early. It's true that those who are left are smart too, but I'm not sure they can help themselves. They mean well. If they quit, this area will go to the dogs. We talk about getting new industry in here to provide employment but we can't save the one we've got. I was talking to one fellow this year. He said, 'I've shifted into high gear and I can't run any faster. If they catch me now I'm done.' A few weeks ago when potatoes were down to a dollar a barrel, the stores right here in Ft. Kent were retailing them at fifty-nine cents a peck — that's six-forty-nine a barrel. When we gave up allotments and price supports we let out the best cow we ever had. The consumer pays the same as he did when the farm price was up."

The most recent Census of Agriculture reports that 685,000 farmers grew 373 million bushels of potatoes on 1.2 million acres in 1959. However, commercial production was chiefly in the hands of just 6,492 specialists, each of whom planted more than 50 acres. This small group raised 66 per cent of the entire crop. Stimulated first by technological progress, then by government price supports, then by knock-down-drag-out competition, production per acre got so high and costs of production so astronomical that most of the little fellows like Paul Rhone finally surrendered while the big operators took over the business.

In Aroostook County today the best potato soils sell for $200 an acre while it costs about $400 an acre to finance a single crop from planting to market.[11] Even if a man mortgaged all his land he could borrow only half the money it takes just to pay one season's costs. Financial assistance on this scale is difficult for most Lower Middle Class farmers to obtain, especially as there is no government price support to reassure the bankers. If a banker refuses a loan, a fertilizer dealer may make an advance if the borrower trades with him, but he will slap a lien on the crop. If a man's credit gets so bad the fertilizer dealers shy away, then the federal Farmers Home Administration may assume the risk of backing him if he has a good reputation. When a man with a good reputation is burned badly, then he, too, is finished.

In today's cutthroat market it is easy to get scorched. Each year more small growers are forced to yield to specialists with stronger financial reserves, more marketing acumen, and lower costs of production. A study of production costs by the Maine Agricultural Experiment Station[11] shows that on the average the farmer pays

$2.78 a barrel to produce potatoes on Lower Middle Class farms with 20 to 29 acres of potatoes, while it costs only $2.11 a barrel on First Class farms with 150 to 330 acres of potatoes. In a tight market 67 cents can easily be the difference between profit and loss. In an ordinary market a 67 cent differential on each of 45,000 to 50,000 barrels, which could be raised on 300 acres, is a fairly tidy sum in itself. This illustrates why large scale production pays off while small scale production often leads to disaster. But it takes more than efficient production to make a successful potato farmer.

Today the smart farmer is one who concentrates as hard on the best way to sell as he does on the best way to produce. This is just old-fashioned business sense but it is surprising how few farmers have it. The marketing angle is important because overproduction is common. The man who can get closest to the buyer in a saturated market has the best chance to make a profitable sale. No farm family is big enough to eat 45,000 bushels of potatoes even if it sent care-packages to all the relatives.

A WINNER

In a game with so many losers there are bound to be winners. We will assume that Wilfred Z. Wilson, a fictitious person who resembles some people in real life, is one of them. Mr. Wilson has a ticker tape in his air-conditioned office at the end of one of several storage houses. Every weekday morning at 10 o'clock he flicks on a switch and a coil of yellow serpentine spins out the prices of Maine potatoes as reported by the New York Mercantile Exchange. Perhaps it is the middle of May and Mr. Wilson has not as yet planted anything but the "Mercantile" is already quoting what buyers will pay for futures from next November through the following April. Mr. Wilson knows pretty well what it will cost him to grow 300 acres of potatoes. He has checked all the current costs: fertilizer, pesticides, machinery, and hired labor. The buyers at the Mercantile have done the same. Fertilizer sales have been checked, government reports on growers' intentions and crop loans have been probed, and some remarks by bankers have not gone unheeded. Mr. Wilson senses there is going to be overproduction again this year.

The buyers on the Mercantile think so too; they are bidding very close to costs of production. Their bids do not satisfy Mr. Wilson but he must stay in business. Before he plants a single acre he wires his broker to sell two-thirds of his future crop at what amounts to a farm price of $2.80 a barrel. This is approximately the break-even point for a majority of small producers. At this price Mr. Wilson thinks he can net 60 cents, but only because he operates on a big scale. While the price is low it will cover a lot of cash expenses and a big risk is already eliminated. Mr. Wilson is fairly certain the price will not go much higher, but he hopes it will. It could dip badly, but he hopes it will not.

Mr. Wilson is a good technician. He is a graduate of the College of Agriculture at Orono. He has been to Idaho and California to visit potato farms and pick up practical ideas. Farmers from the West have been to see his operations in Maine, which now consist of several farms which he bought in recent years from small operators who went out of business. He was careful to purchase only farms with superior soils and good storage facilities even though he paid a premium for them.

As he prepares for the season ahead Mr. Wilson does everything with rigorous care so that he can have all his fields certified for seed if that should eventually prove to be desirable. He maintains active contact with growers he knows in the South who may buy seed stock from him at the usual premium of $1.00 a barrel above the Mercantile's quotations for table quality. If it turns out that the demand for certified seed is strong, Mr. Wilson will sell the remaining third of his crop for that purpose when the time comes. He will even buy back the futures he sold earlier on the Mercantile if the premium on seed potatoes warrants this move.

THE FARMER IN CHAINS

As long as the farm market remains oversupplied, the way a farmer sells is as important as what he does in the field. At the moment the managers of the supermarket chains are in the driver's seat. The technological revolution in merchandising has given the technological revolution in agriculture a headlong shove. Retailers catering to a mass market are in a position to contract for a mass supply at the source, whether that source is a factory or a farm. When food producers and retailers are linked they are almost unbeatable. The farm, or a whole syndicate of farms, is assured of a market for everything grown, and the chain gets its supplies at the lowest possible figure. Chains are hard bargainers because they can afford to be — a buyer who purchases by the carload gets preferences. Chains are hard bargainers because they have to be — they are in competition with one another. Usually, but not always, the consumer is the winner. When chains buy at the farm they cut out brokers, wholesalers, jobbers, salesmen, and bill collectors who otherwise would add their commission to retail costs. Spoilage on fresh items is reduced by direct transfer.

Addressing the Wholesale Section of the Delaware State Chamber of Commerce at Wilmington's Hotel Du Pont, Robert A. Jones, executive vice president of the Middle Atlantic Lumbermen's Association, blasted the chains for by-passing wholesalers and going directly to primary sources for their supplies. "In the not too distant future 50 giant chains will come into being to sell at least 50 per cent of the nation's products at retail," Mr. Jones informed his audience.[12] As far as meat is concerned the "not too distant future" is here, for chains already market more than 50 per cent of this commodity. Production contracts between chains and livestock feeders, or between chains and packers who buy from feeders, are commonplace but as yet only a few chains feed or slaughter their own livestock. In 1961 packers and chains finish-fed only about 5 per cent of all cattle. In the same year chains slaughtered 2½ per cent of all cattle, 3 per cent of all lambs, and 1 per cent of all hogs.[13]

Until recently the small farmer was the traditional livestock feeder. He still is in the corn belt, which remains the prime region for cattle finishing in the nation; but his methods are under severe challenge by integrated chain–packer–feed lot arrangements. It is often said that the big feed lots, which buy most of their feed, cannot finish cattle as cheaply as the small farmer who raises his own hay, silage, and grain. Man for man probably nobody in agriculture accomplishes more by his own physical effort than a Lower Middle Class corn belt farmer. But when it comes to income that is something else again. When he competes with the modern mass feed lot this farmer competes with hired labor and he cannot expect a labor income much higher than the going rate. In addition his operation is smaller and his investment income proportionately less. Usually his overhead cost per unit of livestock is higher. (Tables 3, 10, 13.)

Direct dealing by the mass buyer has had some impact upon the evolution of cattle feeding methods. This practice has helped to stimulate investment in big feed lots which accommodate from 10,000 to 40,000 head of cattle at one time. The precise effect which this development has had on the conventional small farm feeder is not known but an estimate made in 1958 indicated that large feed lots had at that time taken away 10 per cent of the business from Midwest corn-livestock farms.[14] A spot survey in 1961–62 revealed that many ranchers and other cattle raisers have quit the finish-feeding of their own livestock because the margin of profit has dropped. The operators of one mass feed lot in Georgia, which accommodates 40,000 head of cattle, are said to be satisfied with 1 cent of profit on each pound of grain.

Weld County in Colorado ranks second among all counties of the United States as a feeder of cattle and calves. Weld County is located between the range states to the west and the feed grain states to the east. It has its own highly productive irrigated alfalfa fields and the Denver Union Stockyards Company's auctions are a major market. Warren Monfort of the Monfort Feed Lot, Inc. in Weld County sells all his cattle directly to packers.[14] He says this is more profitable because he has "reputation cattle" which the packers know will dress out as top beef. The Monfort Feed Lot, Inc. began as an 80 acre farm a generation ago when Warren's father came as a settler from the corn belt state of Illinois. The farm expanded through the years and today its major feature is 100 acres devoted entirely to feed pens. An average of 40,000 head of cattle and calves pass through these pens, which have feed bunks a quarter of a mile long. Twenty-two thousand head of livestock can be accommodated at one time.

It is impossible for Mr. Monfort to raise enough supplies on his own land. Consequently he contracts with fifty other farms in the Weld County area to provide him with feed. He has a grain elevator with a half-million-bushel capacity on his home ground and another elevator in Nebraska which holds a million bushels. On his staff is a veterinarian as well as thirty other employees who operate machinery and feed the livestock. He says his operation "is a sort of roll back across the mountains from California. Out there they didn't have to unlearn anything such as we do in changing from the small farm feed lot. They started with big feed lots . . ."

What the conventional small grain-livestock enterprise has lost to the mass feed lots in the past is nothing compared with what lies ahead. Profit margins all along the line are under fire and only those who can survive on small margins through mass production will endure. That is unless the small operators, who can outvote the big ones, call in the government to set up quotas and allotments. The fights between big and small cotton farms will seem like child's play compared with the contests looming ahead when the livestockmen lock horns. The present debate on farm policy exposes the conflict in positions. At present feed is surplus whereas livestock, particularly beef, is in demand. The big livestock interests which buy feed are against production controls that would enhance the value of feed relative to the value of livestock. They support the Farm Bureau platform of no allotments and low price supports. Small farmers who finish livestock with their home-grown feed generally favor high price supports. These farmers prefer the viewpoint of the National Farmers Organization and the Farmers Union.

Big feed lots require such enormous quantities of operating capital that most of their operators cannot finance themselves. Many feed lot owners are really piece workers who make a very small profit on each unit of a huge output. Most banks will not touch them if they do not have contracts or contacts. In such a situation the chains are salvation itself. Either by their direct purchases or by their arrangements with packers the chains stabilize the market.

As long as real competition exists among the chains they will not become major feeders because it is doubtful if they could do the job more cheaply than it is now done. Since their business is retailing and not production, the chains' objective is a stable supply at the lowest possible price. This they get when they establish a satisfactory arrangement directly with feeders or with packers who have arrangements with feeders. The banks which advance capital to feeders attach considerable importance to the character and history of these arrangements.

The average farmer in the Lower Middle Class generally limits feeding to the extent of the supplies he harvests from his own fields. Because he feeds only a few units, profit is likely to be low. His overhead costs are relatively high and his labor income is substandard. This is not the best possible position to be in, at least in a competitive economy.

FREE LANCE

New England vegetable farmer Elmer Woody is eloquent when he recounts how he lost some battles but won his private war with the chain supermarkets. "I come from a long line of rural people.

Every one of them had to find a novel way to make a living or he would have gone under. I guess I had to maintain the family tradition." With this preamble Mr. Woody began to relate how, in an age of conformity, he developed the survival tactics which enabled him to remain an independent small farmer.

"My grandfather started commercial farming when most country people were subsistence cultivators. He built the first greenhouse in this part of the state and developed an old swamp into a cranberry bog. He did well with cranberries but overshot his mark on grapes. He planted grapes because he liked them, but they didn't sell. There were no Italians here then to make wine and Yankees preferred cider. Grandfather hauled the grapes to a dump in an oxcart. He was born a hundred years too soon, but he was imaginative. My father was more practical. He produced what he could sell. He raised vegetables and peddled them store to store. In 1912 he made a truck out of an old Maxwell car. It was the first farm truck around here. On Sundays he hauled members of the Elks Club and their families to the beach. It was fun and he made money."

When Elmer Woody tells his story he does not fail to mention the little things that make a difference on the rough road to achievement. "Dad bought a telephone as soon as one was available. With that he was able to get orders from the stores before we picked. There were eight or ten other farms competing with him and it helped to know in advance what our customers wanted on any particular day. About the late 1940's the chains came in. At first we sold to the managers of the individual supermarkets. Then, as the organization cornered more of the local trade, it set up a single buyer for all of its stores. We never saw him. He was a voice on the phone. At first he asked us what we had and what we wanted for it. Later he'd specify varieties and quantities and he'd tell us what he would pay. Little by little the whole system changed. The chains employed efficiency experts and the buyers got tougher.

"Soon we were eased into pre-packaging at the farm. When we

arrived at the stores with everything nicely prepared, the managers would ask us to lay our produce out on the retail racks. They said they were short of help. The chains wouldn't pay anything for these services that took our time. They said we could hire help cheaper than they could. The few independent grocers who were left began to demand the same treatment. In the beginning the chains paid promptly every Tuesday. Later they pushed back our payday a full month. We always prided ourselves on fine quality but the supermarkets would not pay premiums. They wanted everything the same size, the same weight, and the same color and shape — nothing poor, nothing exceptional, everything good average. They don't want shoppers pawing over articles. They want the housewife to take the first thing she sees and move on. If there is a noticeable difference in quality she will go through the whole works.

"For a while we tried to develop a specialty trade in the chain stores. When we stocked their display racks we would stick up a sign saying GROWN BY WOODY'S MARKET GARDENS. We wanted customers to notice the superiority of our products and choose them. When we came back the next day we would find Jersey and Connecticut produce under our signs. The manager would say it was the fault of some clerk. I gave up. I could see that if we stayed with the chains we would have to do it their way. We would have to specialize in two or three crops and set ourselves up to trim, grade, package and wax on an assembly line. We would have to use all the tricks the chains had learned in California. Their system of packaging swept New England in just two years. Some vegetables will keep for weeks in plastic sheaths and still look good even though they taste like wood."

Mr. Woody is not a man to burn his bridges injudiciously. "I knew if we specialized and standardized, the customer wouldn't be able to tell the difference between home-grown and shipped-in produce. That would put us in competition with Jersey. I spent a couple of days down there at Seabrook Farms and came home with my tail between my legs. Our fifty acres of vegetables wouldn't stand a chance." Seabrook Farms grow, pack and freeze over a million pounds of vegetables daily during the summer season. To supplement harvests from its own thousands of acres Seabrook has contracts for additional supplies with scores of little farms like Mr. Woody's in New Jersey and nearby Delaware, Maryland, and Pennsylvania. Elmer Woody was paralyzed by what he saw.

"I knew I had to find a new way to retail our produce. I decided to set up a roadside stand on my place. The transition was hard. I had to learn what would sell and how to sell it. The roadside market is different from the store market. I knew that quality would be my only asset. I irrigate. It is one of the keys to quality. Never let vegetables slow down once they start to grow or they'll acquire a tough fiber. I have to retrain people's taste. Today's consumers are guided more by appearance than anything else. A generation ago they knew enough to ask for Green Mountain potatoes, Nantes carrots, Detroit Dark Red beets, and Sparkles strawberries. These may be poor yielders; they may not keep well, freeze well, or present the best appearance, but for flavor they are without equal. I have a reputation for tomatoes. Glamour is my favorite. It has a thin skin. The chains want a variety with a skin as thick as a rhinoceros hide. People will buy corn in stores with a shell so tough it will snap back when you bite it. We grow Barbecue. You can't handle it roughly or the kernels will pop.

"I was afraid at first when we broke away from the chains but now I'm glad. Regular customers come from as much as forty miles away. Women pool their orders and take turns driving here to get a week's supply of fresh vegetables. To do a good job of roadside selling you must do the opposite of what the supermarkets are doing. We don't package anything. We accept a ten per cent loss from handling because people like that privilege. It's one of our selling points. The janes with the long fingernails can't resist jabbing them into things to test them. After they're satisfied they leave the ones they've speared and buy others, but we let it pass. If we sold only to husbands I could retire in five years. Men are crazy for fresh vegetables. Women are budget-conscious. What we like most are the carloads of commuters on their way home from a factory. They're hungry; they've been eating out of a tin pail. They can't resist the temptation to load up for supper. I see no limit to the possibilities of a roadside market if a farmer is on a traveled highway like I am and if he specializes in quality rather than mediocrity."

THE BROADER SCENE

In the broader picture of American agriculture potato culture and vegetable growing are fringe activities but we have already noted that the trends toward concentration and specialization which induced Paul Rhone to quit and which almost eliminated Elmer Woody are characteristic of nearly all the major segments of husbandry: a comparatively small number of farms in the First Class usually dominate the field. The great mass of cultivators in the Lower Middle Class have a relatively small piece of the market. Statistics which show the degree of concentration in various types of farming are presented in Table 3. From these data it is apparent that tobacco culture is the one type of farming which is still the stronghold of the small farm: 65 per cent of the market remains in the hands of the Lower Middle Class, which is 90 per cent of all specialized tobacco producers. However, these growers are less than 4 per cent of all husbandmen.

The Lower Middle Class makes a fair showing in general farming with 34 per cent of all sales. As dairy specialists this class accounts for 31 per cent of marketed produce. In cash grain it sells 28 per cent, and it markets 22 per cent of livestock other than poultry. Considering the very large numbers of farms in the Lower Middle Class, these percentages reflect weakness rather than strength. It is no coincidence that the producers of these commodities are now making the loudest appeals for federal help. They are severely wounded and their hold on the market is slipping faster than their own net decline in numbers. The evolution toward gigantism which has squeezed the Lower Middle Class down to negligible proportions in vegetables (7 per cent), ranching (13 per cent), poultry (12 per cent), and fruit and nuts (13 per cent) is now progressing in the other departments.

The basic difficulty among most distressed farmers is not that prices are low but that they produce such a small share of the total marketed supply. There is no reasonable way to raise their incomes as long as their position in the market continues to erode. In this discussion the Third Class of pseudo farmers has not even been considered since as a group these 44 per cent of all census "farmers" sell 5 per cent of all agricultural produce.

In contrast to the position of the middle classes is the excellent standing of First Class farms. Their absolute numbers are very small but, as Table 3 indicates, their share of the market is often remarkably large: 84 per cent in vegetables, 75 per cent in livestock ranching, 73 per cent in fruits and nuts, 70 per cent in poultry, and 63 per cent in cotton. Just as important as this present dominance is the fact that their market position is growing stronger in other specialties.

FREE ADVICE

College administrators have a trick which some of them like to pull at the first assembly of each freshman class. To impress new recruits with ivory tower standards, one of the deans delivers a stick-and-carrot speech. At an opportune point in his address the speaker requests each student to look first to the person on his right, then to the person on his left. After a pause, he declares with a cheshire grin that before four years are over one of the shining faces on either side will have flunked out. Farmers have been looking at each other like that for some time. They do not find it a bit funny.

THE DISTRESSED

On August 28, 1962 thousands of midwestern farmers who were feeling the pinch of competition assembled in Des Moines, Iowa to hear Oren Lee Staley, president of the National Farmers Organization, deliver a rousing speech on "holding actions." By midnight August 31 the NFO's national membership was set to launch a sales strike which they hoped would force processors to pay higher prices for farm commodities. As if to emulate organized labor, they had chosen the long Labor Day weekend on which to begin withholding livestock and grains from the market. This militant decision was just one more move on the part of organized agriculture to increase its "take-home pay" and to establish the NFO as a union for collective bargaining with packers and millers. The protesting farmers had long been disillusioned with federal agricultural policy and were eager to take matters into their own hands. The NFO agreed with critics who said that a successful strike would raise consumer prices, but it contended that collective bargaining could eliminate the need for taxpayer price supports.[15]

The strike lasted thirty-two days. Enough livestock was temporarily withheld to close down some small slaughterhouses. The big packers laid off several hundred workers. A spokesman for Armour and Co. explained that "You can't run a packing plant without hogs." Just as the strike got off the ground packers raised yard quotations $\frac{1}{2}$ to 1 cent a pound to encourage deliveries by non-strikers.[16] Retailers, capitalizing on newspaper reports of shut-downs, boosted their markups 5 to 10 cents a pound, whereupon whatever consumer sympathy there may have been for the farmer quickly evaporated. When the U. S. cost of living index for September rose six-tenths of one per cent, the Commissioner of Labor Statistics, Ewan Clague, attributed most of the increase to the NFO's holding action.[17] The NFO had reason to believe that its tactics were succeeding. Mr. Staley announced that "Enthusiasm of members and non-members for our holding action makes me think we may get results sooner than we expected."[18]

Skeptics, particularly leaders of the American Farm Bureau Federation, denounced the strike and predicted its failure. Charles B. Shuman, president of the Farm Bureau, declared that "withholding products from the market after they have been produced is not an effective solution."[19] As already noted, it is Farm Bureau policy to encourage production management through farmer-run cooperatives which set quotas, establish quality standards, and fix prices before their produce is sent to processors. Three weeks after the NFO withholding action had begun President Staley told the press: "... we now feel we'll soon be in the driver's seat."[20]

By the fifth week it was apparent that the strike had failed and on October 2 it was officially "recessed." Too many farmers in disagreement with the NFO had continued to ship to processors; some stockmen had even increased their deliveries to take advantage of the slight rise in wholesale prices. Bitter antagonisms developed within farm communities. Fence wires were cut, truck tires were shot up, and barns were reportedly burned; neighbors and relatives fell out with one another over the strike issue.[21]

The NFO claimed to have been tipped off that a meat processor planned to bring "thugs out of New York to show these farmers something."[22] On the other hand, one farm magazine[23] suggested that non-strikers should ship during the strike while prices were higher and proffered a bit of fraternal advice to its readers: "Of course, you should be reminded that this is a Walter Reuther-UAW-backed bunch ($1,000 per week) so they will probably have the usual union-type goons in their picket lines. It might be a good idea to carry your shotgun along to encourage them out of your way and knock them off your truck as you go to the yards."

Although NFO's withholding action was a failure, its implications will be debated for some time to come. Certainly this was not the last aggressive move that farmers would make to get a bigger share of the food dollar. It was abundantly clear to those who understand farm politics that while a tactic had failed, an objective remained.

The NFO's principal objective had been to secure long-term market contracts with processors which would fix wholesale prices at higher levels. The strike aimed to raise processors' prices for choice grade cattle from $28.00 to $32.45; for top grade hogs from $18.25 to $22.75; and for corn from $1.11 a bushel to $1.49. However, a more important goal was to secure a guarantee that these higher prices would remain in effect for a stipulated period. To a less sanguine person than Oren Lee Staley this would have loomed as an insurmountable task in view of agriculture's excessive capacity to produce. Mr. Staley once estimated that all the farmers in the NFO and those "signing up with us" account for 25 to 30 per cent of the nation's production of hogs, beef, lambs, corn, and soybeans. He indicated that this share of the total supply would be enough to influence market prices if all of it were sold under contract, but he also acknowledged: "We'd probably need around 60 per cent to be the controlling factor."[24]

CONSUMER INTEREST

In an open letter to the Secretary of Agriculture,[25] Congressman James Roosevelt of California protested that "If the strike is a success, it will raise the price of pork to consumers by at least 16 per cent . . . A further increase — set artificially by a small group of producers — would put a tremendous burden on the food budgets of millions of consumers." An intensified conflict between town and country over arbitrary food price-fixing, whether by government or by organized agriculture, loomed on the nation's horizon.

Apparently Congressman Roosevelt was among the first lawmakers to recognize that as farmers become fewer in number, but more substantial and better organized, the present era of uncontrolled production of cheap food may give way to one in which highly capitalized agriculturalists ration production privileges among themselves and set prices at whatever levels the traffic will bear. Thus, in his letter to the Secretary of Agriculture, he said, "The National Farmers Organization is trying to insure the withdrawal from the market of a number of important consumer and commercial food products until it has signed contracts with major processors of these products guaranteeing minimum prices which they, the producers, have set arbitrarily and without any apparent consideration of the interests of the millions of consumers who must eat these products."

THE STRIKER

Who was the NFO striker? This is a question which *Wallaces Farmer,* Iowa's leading farm journal, sought to answer by sending its reporters into the field to collect statistics. The returns[26] showed him to be a small operator — the kind who has been by-passed by the technologically advanced. Among other things, the editors of *Wallaces Farmer* discovered that a willingness to withhold hogs from the market and stand with the NFO was most evident among farmers with the smallest operations. Such willingness faded as the size of operation increased. Of those who normally market less than 100 hogs annually, 36 per cent stuck with NFO for the duration of the withholding action. Of farmers selling between 100 and 499 hogs annually, 28 per cent complied with the NFO strike call. The really big producers who sell over 500 hogs annually practically ignored the protest; only 10 per cent of them participated.*

It would seem that for the most part the NFO withholding action was a move of desperation by the frustrated marginal agriculturist of the Lower Middle Class who is inclined to attribute his troubles to low market prices instead of to the fact that he and his undercapitalized farm are obsolete.

NFO members were reluctant to admit it, but it was clear that most of the big, efficient farmers who continued to deliver during the heat of the controversy were not strikebreakers following the advice of the Farm Bureau. They had not favored the strike in the first place and had not pledged themselves to join it. They were satisfied with the free market price as it had existed before the

---

* According to the 1959 Census of Agriculture the top 1 per cent of all hog farmers, each of whom marketed over 500 animals, produced more pork than the bottom 51 per cent of all hog farmers, each of whom marketed less than 30 animals.

strike; the very magnitude of their operations indicated that they were able to make a satisfactory income by producing a large volume for a small margin of profit per unit. They disagreed for practical as well as for philosophical reasons with those who thought the way out for a large but depressed segment of American agriculture was to raise prices rather than to increase efficiency.

Lauren Soth, editor of the *Des Moines Register and Tribune* and a leading commentator on midwestern agriculture, has characterized the NFO withholding action as a move by the small farmer to protect his livelihood. "The N.F.O. patrols," said Soth, "which, last September, tried to persuade or intimidate farmers to keep their hogs and cattle off the market, were striking for higher prices that would enable the small farmer to stay on the farm." Referring to his home state of Iowa, editor Soth said: "These people have always been the staunchest of Republican conservatives — even Eisenhower was a little too leftish for them. . . . Both the N.F.O. and its businessmen backers, however, are a small minority in the state — the minority which always, in all societies, wants to halt change. They represent the people who feel left out and find it difficult to adapt."[27]

During the period of the withholding action a few urbanites sensed how helpless they might be if farmers became so well organized that they could desert the free enterprise system and initiate a closed price-control system of their own. The NFO had asserted when the strike began that "Farmers have less than 10 per cent of the vote but 100 per cent of the food."[22] Mr. Staley had also made it clear that the purpose of the strike was to "get ourselves in a position where we would be as effective as industry in pricing and as effective as labor in bargaining."[24]

Chapter 3

The Farm in the
American Mind

When ninety-year-old bachelor John William Knight of Galla-
tin, Missouri was a young farmer it was necessary to work to
make "ends meet" and a big mortgage, instead of being a status
symbol, was a terror to contemplate. Since Mr. Knight was born
in another century, when farmers paid more in taxes than they received in government aid, he developed a jaundiced view of public
finance. "I've hated the Government ever since I was old enough
to know anything," farmer Knight divulged some time ago when
he decided to give away his estate rather than let the inheritance
tax take a bite. "I was raised in a log house on a ridge about three
miles west of here. First farm I bought was the old Blake place.
Drove $200 worth of cattle and hogs up there to make the first pay-
ment." That was an auspicious beginning for a young man, but
the shock of adversity was to follow. "Right off they wanted $45
taxes on the place and it [was] still mortgaged. It don't hardly
seem right," complained Mr. Knight, "a man has to pay taxes on
a farm he don't even own."[1] This was his way of looking at things

then. During the past ninety years a lot of ideas have changed and some have grown old like Mr. Knight.

AVANT-GARDE

When the little man with the hoe retreats from the countryside, he may contrive a refuge in the city for his rustic spirit. Mr. and Mrs. James M. Smith of Columbus, Ohio have shown one way this can be done. Exhibiting that love of the soil which runs deep in the American psyche, the Smiths slowly, and a little at a time, managed to lug ten tons of rich corn belt earth to the rooftop of their apartment building by way of the fire escape. There with the help of rain and warm midwestern sunshine, they created a garden out of an asphalt wilderness. What the Smiths will do if crop controls oblige them to put their land in the soil bank is a problem they have not yet wrestled with.

FLASHBACK

In 1782 there was published in London a folio of letters by J. Hector St. John Crèvecoeur,[2] self-styled "simple cultivator of the earth," which portrayed an idyllic kind of rural life in the America of that day. Here was expressed eloquently the joy and contentment of a free man in a new society which offered European peasants a chance to be independent on their own land. "I bless God," wrote Crèvecoeur of Carlisle in Pennsylvania, "for all the good he has given me; I envy no man's prosperity, and with no other portion of happiness than that I may live to teach the same philosophy to my children; and give each of them a farm, shew them how to cultivate it, and be like their father, good substantial independent American farmers — an appellation which will be the most fortunate one, a man of my class can possess, so long as our civil government continues to shed blessings on our husbandry."

Such enchanting accounts of daily life on the soil helped to create, over the years, a popular image of the noble family farmer that still persists in the American mind. Crèvecoeur told his readers:

"We have no princes, for whom we toil, starve, and bleed: we are the most perfect society now existing in the world." Material achievements he described as modest but adequate: "A pleasing uniformity of decent competence appears throughout our habitations. The meanest of our log-houses is a dry and comfortable habitation."

In telling of his good fortune, Crèvecoeur did not neglect to inform his readers that he had a little help: "My father left me three hundred and seventy-one acres of land, forty-seven of which are good timothy meadow, and excellent orchard, a good house, and a substantial barn. It is my duty to think how happy I am that he lived to build and to pay for all these improvements. What are the labours which I have to undergo, what are my fatigues when compared to his, who had every thing to do, from the first tree he felled to the finishing of his house? . . . what can I wish more? My negroes are tolerably faithful and healthy; by a long series of industry and honest dealings, my father left behind him the name of a good man; I have but to tread his paths to be happy and a good man like him." Crèvecoeur remarked that his slaves were "well clad," "well fed," and "not obliged to work more than white people." Of course their opinion of the life of a "simple cultivator of the earth" may have had a twist of its own.

The historian A. Whitney Griswold, in his book *Farming and Democracy*,[3] reminds us that the idyllic concept of the family farm has been cherished so long that it is widely and uncritically accepted as an essential ingredient in American culture. Rural man is believed to be incorruptibly democratic and free of subservience to wealth or power. Thomas Jefferson, together with other political philosophers of his time, helped to develop this concept. Having observed the misery of the English peasantry, Jefferson thought that Americans could avoid a similar fate if each family had a farm of its own to assure its independence and virtue: "Those who labor in the earth are the chosen people of God, if ever He had a chosen people, whose breasts He has made His peculiar deposit for substantial and genuine virtue. Corruption of morals in the mass of cultivators is a phenomenon of which no age nor nation has furnished an example."[4]

Even in this machine age legislative halls reverberate with oratorical compliments for the family man of the soil. Apropos of recent federal programs for agriculture the magazine *Time* observed, "Many defenders of the price-support system argue it is needed to preserve the family farm, that disappearance of the family farm would weaken the moral fabric of the nation."[5]

Griswold suggests: "If democracy is to survive we must believe in it, not as a myth but as reality; and if we believe in it as reality we can hold no theoretical proposition of democracy too lightly to consider it as fact."[3] He cites the opening sentences of Bulfinch's *Mythology* to press his point: "The religions of ancient Greece and Rome are extinct. The so-called divinities of Olympus have not a single worshipper among living men." If democracy is to avoid the destiny of a faith that fades into mythology, its interpretation must have reality. It must either evolve with the times or be lost like the gods of Olympus. If, at a time when farm families are so rapidly leaving the soil and 92 per cent of the population lives elsewhere, we continue to regard the family farm as a pillar of democracy, we may wake up to find the roof has caved in.

OFFICIAL VIEWPOINT

Some Washington officials deny that the family farm is fading. For example, at a recent convocation of farm leaders and research workers at the Department of Agriculture in Washington,[7] guests were informed that "contrary to the opinion of many, family farms are becoming increasingly important in our agriculture." In support of this viewpoint it was noted that between 1949 and 1959 there had been a 104 per cent increase in "adequate" family farms and a decrease of 50 per cent in "inadequate" family farms. These data suggest a favorable "balance of trade," but the net figures behind the percentages tell a different story. While the number of "adequate" family farms increased from 334,000 to 680,000, the number of "inadequate" family farms declined from 3,138,000 to 1,582,000. It must have been a consolation to the audience to learn that while the farm family is on its way to oblivion the family farm is doing better than ever.

At the same conference a representative of the Department of Agriculture attempted to explain how family farms are becoming increasingly important in our agriculture despite a loss of over a million farm families in ten years. Said he, "The rapid adoption of technology in agriculture, with its accompanying transformation to a highly capitalized, efficient industry has had less undermining impact on the family farm than is frequently believed. The family farm has proved to be sufficiently flexible and amenable to change to permit it to retain, and even enhance, its position." To this observation the speaker added some qualifications. ". . . however," he said, "we need to define the institution to which we refer as the family farm. We need also to distinguish clearly in our thinking between 'adequate' and 'inadequate' family farms."

As described by the Washington official, the family farm has two essential characteristics. It is a farm business in which the farm family provides at least half the labor and most of the management. Also, "It has no ownership or tenancy attribute because acquisition of management control is independent of ownership." This is the modern way to say it can be a tenant farm. "Adequate" family farms, as the Department of Agriculture sees them, are those with gross sales of over $10,000; "inadequate" units are those with gross sales of less. Few would dispute this division. Farms grossing over $10,000 are in the First and Upper Middle Classes; those grossing less are in the Third and Lower Middle Classes and by modern standards they are definitely inadequate. In 1959 the "adequate" family farms and others in the First and Upper Middle Classes had average real estate investments of $135,000 and

$57,000 respectively. The "inadequate" family farms in the Lower Middle and Third Classes had average real estate investments of $27,000 and $11,000 respectively. (Table 13.)

What is puzzling about this presentation is the conclusion that "The family farm has proved to be sufficiently flexible and amenable to change to permit it to retain, and even to enhance, its position." It is a little hard to see how this follows from the fact that the class of farm on the increase is less numerous, more highly capitalized, and more dependent upon tenant management and hired help than the farm which is expiring. For every well-capitalized "adequate" family farm that joins the ranks of the saved, 3.5 "inadequate" modestly capitalized family farms that are more dependent on family labor go down the drain. (See Tables 4, 9, 11, 12, 13.) But the taxpayer might wish to believe he is paying to save the family farm, and there are statistics aplenty which would lead him to think that he is. Perhaps it all looks very progressive in some statistics, but the statistician may not have looked into the eyes of the wounded.

CHAIN REACTION

In the spring of 1962 Representative J. Floyd Breeding of Kansas commented on the decline in the number of farms in his home state. "What has transformed farming into the 'farm problem,'" said the congressman, "is simply that the change has come here first and most dramatically. Fuss about the disappearing family farm or any other phase of the problem you wish, but what it all adds up to is technological unemployment in agriculture. It requires only a very few of us to produce the food and fiber for all the rest of us. Those who otherwise might be employed in agriculture, now must find other places than the farm to live, other jobs than farming to do. The result has been a vast, unprecedented social and economic upheaval, the effects of which no one has yet begun to measure."[8]

In the autumn of 1962 Representative Breeding met up with the problem of the congressman in a depopulated rural area. The declining farm population of Kansas had resulted in the loss of one of the state's six congressional districts. In a run-off election to see who would be eliminated, Mr. Breeding became technologically unemployed.

A SURVIVOR

There is no confusion about what is a family farm in the mind of Mrs. Beth Scheib of Soap Lake, Washington. Pretty widow Scheib, whose husband died in a plane crash, cultivates 10 acres of her own and 65 acres belonging to a neighbor. Her hired help is a baby sitter employed while her own daughters are in school. In the field and in the barn Beth Scheib is assisted by her twelve children aged 2 months to 14 years. "I couldn't hire a man for fifty cents an hour and I couldn't pay more." Every Scheib works, even baby Larry, whose dependent cries remind his older brothers and sisters not to loaf. When her husband died, Mrs. Scheib was urged to forsake the farm for a town job. "The bankers, Farm Home Administration advisers and everyone else told me to sell out and move to town," Mrs. Scheib recalls with evident pride. "What could I do in town with twelve children? For the price of a year's payment on the farm I couldn't even rent a house. I'm trying it my own way." Beth Scheib's own way means both field work and house work, although after school her eldest son takes charge in the fields. Everyone has tasks and all work together whenever possible, whether it is at irrigating the crops or feeding the livestock — and all are happy that they are a family of farmers on a family farm.[9]

COUNTERATTACK

In the spring of 1962, as pavement-bound urbanites were feeling an elemental urge to return to the soil, J. M. Bess of the Syndication Investors Management Company announced a way to restore them to agriculture. At a conference sponsored by International Business Machines at Endicott, New York, Mr. Bess explained how a family with a small sum to invest could acquire a share in a Black Angus cattle ranch to be established in Dutchess County, New York.[10] He indicated that realty interests, particularly in the West and South, had developed considerable enthusiasm for such farm syndicates and that the idea was spreading. Mr. Bess said his company hoped to net its investors 15 per cent annually. This return might be expected, he explained, because federal programs, designed to help the small farmer, provide liberal tax allowances on farm property and breeding stock. Also, profits from the sale of certain farm assets are taxable only at capital gains rates. As Mr. Bess informed his audience, this generates a cash flow from which distributions can be made.

In line with such up-to-date appraisals of farm opportunity for the city family, a prominent financial advisory service recently told subscribers how to make profits in agriculture without earning money. While most farmers cannot do this, outside investors can if they are in the right tax bracket. Explained the financial wizards by way of example, just convert $50,000 ordinary income, which would be taxed at 65 per cent, into capital gains of $50,000, taxed at 25 per cent, and you have made $20,000. Apparently it is a way to succeed in agriculture without really trying. Roughly the system is said to work like this: Mr. Roe, an executive in the 65 per cent tax bracket, buys feed, hires labor, and rents land and breeding stock from a rancher, Mr. Doe, at $10,000 a year for five years. During this time Roe sells the offspring, or the offspring of offspring, from his rented cows as breeding stock, taxable at capital gains rates. Assuming investor Roe sells $50,000 worth of breeding cattle, he gets back not a cent more than he paid rancher Doe for this service. But through his non-profit organization Roe saves the $20,000 net. The old-fashioned son of the soil has yet to learn how to do well in agriculture.

OTHER TRADITIONS

While the small family farm has been idolized in the public mind since colonial times, it was never free from challenge by competitive agricultural systems. Now that this cherished institution is losing its membership so rapidly the American mind is distressed. It seems that a haven from everyman's economic storm is being undermined; that a rampart to defend the independent spirit has been breached. Recent decades have seen too many Americans abandon rural security because it is no longer secure. It is hard for the common man to admit to himself that his future lies in a city job on someone else's payroll. The struggle for a comprehensive Social Security system and for genuine rather than token civil rights is part of urban man's search for independence now that the door to opportunity in agriculture is going the way of opportunity in "Pop and Mom" shopkeeping.

Possibly part of the impetus behind suburban expansion in recent decades has been a feeling that city employment need not imply a complete forfeiture of country living. It may wound the job-holder's pride to know he will always be just another hired man, but he recovers some dignity through ownership of a home and lot in suburbia. One of the urgent tasks of contemporary industrial-city culture is to create within its own context compensatory values to replace those destroyed by the passing of the small family farm. Since one agricultural worker is able now to feed himself and 25 other persons, and this ratio soon will be 1 to 50, it is clear that the farm can never again become the bulwark of social or economic democracy that it was in 1776 when 9 persons out of every 10 lived on the soil. Fresh thinking about new institutions for an urban age is called for rather than a facile redefinition of the family farm to make it appear that its social significance remains unaltered.

THE IMPACT OF HISTORY

In recent years, as currents of change swept across the landscape, they unavoidably sketched new patterns while erasing the old. These new designs also have historical antecedents, but, like a weedy garden, they did not begin to thrive until competition was removed. The small family farm which inspired the hopes of common men for many decades was only one of several kinds of agricultural organization established by colonial settlers. Another was the Spanish hacienda, which now, after a long siesta, is coming into its own although in a much modified form. As the story of American agriculture is usually told, the impact of Spanish institutions is minimized except in the Southwest where it is easy to observe. Although St. Augustine and Santa Fé were founded before Jamestown and Plymouth, very few Spaniards came to settle in what is now the United States. It is not surprising, therefore, that Spanish systems of land management long remained in the background of the American scene where English colonial systems monopolized the center of attention.

In territories which fell under Spanish domination, agriculture differed both in method and design from the way it developed in English settlements. The conquistadors were militarists and religious fanatics, not farmers, financiers, or religious refugees. Having driven the Moors from Spain in a holy war that ended the year Columbus discovered America, these aggressive opportunists turned to America as offering the best prospect for professional military activity and quick rewards. The objective of the generals and the crown was not to invest Spanish wealth in the pursuit of trade and the development of plantations. The objective of the foot soldiers was not to secure land on which to become subsistence settlers. Rather, the ambition of all Spaniards, high and low, was to acquire wealth by making Indians produce it for them. Grants of land and permits to use conquered Indians as laborers were the usual compensation awarded to those who participated in successful assaults.

THE HACIENDA AND ENCOMIENDA

Two institutions, the *hacienda* and the *encomienda,* formed the economic basis of prosperous Spanish settlement from Mexico to Peru. Haciendas were tracts of land. The encomiendas were assignments of Indians to work the soil. A hacienda without a sizable encomienda was of little value to a landlord unless he turned to ranching. Thus, in the territory which eventually was to become part of the United States, the Spaniards made comparatively little progress at farming. They had plenty of land, and even in dry areas there were valleys which might have been irrigated, but there were few sedentary, agricultural Indians to impress into service. The more resourceful Indians of the eastern woodlands and the western plains generally resisted peonage.

It was Christopher Columbus who first instituted the encomienda in America when he decreed that subdued tribes should assign Indians in sufficient number to develop and maintain the haciendas of his conquistadors. Technically the encomienda Indians were not slaves as were the Africans on English plantations. They were not purchased and so did not represent a capital outlay. Usually they lived in their own tribal villages or pueblos, where they had gardens and maintained themselves without expense to the *hacendados*. Some haciendas had Indian villages within their bounds, but the lives and customs of the people were not otherwise affected as long as they fulfilled their work tasks and religious duties. As for economic rewards, those of peonage did not differ substantially from those of slavery.

All the great Spanish adventurers who came to this country, from Ponce de Leon to Juan de Oñate, suffered defeat or disappointment in their search for wealth. They found land in abundance, and even gold in Arizona, but they never conquered enough Indians advanced in mining, handicrafts, or agriculture to make it worth while for persons of their eminence to remain. Only less pretentious missions and presidios, under orders from distant viceroys, made permanent settlements, and these were of little account commercially.

The nineteenth century advance of the Anglo-Saxon frontier changed the picture. It heralded a new type of economy and new kinds of opportunity for those who possessed land. By 1848, when the Southwest from Texas to California had become wholly

United States territory, keen Anglo-Saxon adventurers and specu-
lators had already been on the scene gathering titles to vast holdings. They had connived with susceptible Latin bureaucrats to secure hacienda grants in the best locations. By the terms of the
treaty of Guadalupe Hidalgo which ended the Mexican War, titles
to these properties were validated by the United States and the
groundwork was laid for the development of a special kind of
large scale agriculture quite different from the family farm of the
Jeffersonian tradition. In California alone 800 Americans acquired
8 million acres from Mexico at a time when 160 acres was considered a suitable family homestead in the northeastern United
States. It is to be noted, however, that in some sections of the South
slave plantations compared roughly with haciendas in size.

THE HACIENDA AND INDUSTRIAL AGRICULTURE

After the Civil War the growth of cities, manufacturing, and
commerce in the former Spanish-Mexican territories created ever
greater markets for agricultural produce. The potentialities inher-
ent in this situation were first exploited in California. There urban
populations multiplied with astounding rapidity and demands for
food increased with equal suddenness. Within two and one-half
decades San Francisco grew to over a third of a million people. It
had taken Boston two and one-half centuries to do as well. With
its best lands already allocated to haciendas, California was in no
position to welcome family homesteaders to small family plots in
the generous eastern manner. Nor did this fact reduce local re-
sourcefulness. The big properties, with huge new markets at their
doorstep, had every inducement to innovate mass production
methods, particularly in wheat culture. For the first time industrial
techniques were applied to farming. By the end of the nineteenth
century the steam tractor had brought power to the fields while
seasonal work was performed by hordes of migrant "hobo" labor.
The hacienda was finally supplied with a labor force — a modern
version of the encomienda.

It has taken several decades to perfect the field methods, financial devices, and labor recruitment techniques of industrialized agriculture as first practiced in California. Now that these have been polished to a fine routine, the hacienda is in a good position to challenge farms that are operated chiefly with family labor. It has already vanquished the southeastern tenant-sharecropper cotton plantations which replaced slave estates after the Civil War (Tables 3, 10). Tenant family labor equipped with a mule and primitive implements could not compete with an encomienda of thousands of imported low-wage Mexican peons paced by power machinery. In the past twenty years the largest plantations of Black Belt Alabama and the Mississippi Delta have dismissed their tenants and shifted either to cattle or to hacienda-style mechanized operations supplemented by seasonal encomienda. (See Table 10.) Now the Lower Middle Class commercial farm which is too modestly capitalized to adopt some of the techniques of big-scale agriculture is finding itself in difficulty. The Upper Middle Class farm which is adopting these more efficient methods is doing better. There is no indication in the census that large scale industrial agriculture will cease to proliferate and extend its territory, although it will make slower headway in cash grains, dairying, and livestock feeding. (Table 3.)

Since its beginnings in California, hacienda agriculture has assumed a number of ingenious shapes and developed nuclei in every major agricultural region of the nation. It is the wave of the future. Many haciendas are family-owned and they are included among those units which the Department of Agriculture calls "adequate" family farms.

THE HACIENDA CHANGES

Contemporary American versions of the hacienda are, of course, drastically different from anything conceived of by the conquistadors in the age of Indian hand labor, when not even the horse had been introduced to farm work except as a mount for field overseers and cowboys. The top 3 per cent of all farms, each of which markets more than $40,000 worth of commodities annually (Table 1), come closer to the hacienda concept than do any other operations designated in the Census of Agriculture. Although acreage alone is not a sufficient criterion of today's hacienda, the average size of these large enterprises is 2,466 acres, or ten times that of all other census farms, which is 240 acres.[11] Forty-five per cent of all farms with five tractors or more are in this group.[11] To the extent that machines replace manpower they become the modern equivalent of the encomienda.

The big farms as a group are the big buyers of other types of machinery and of chemicals, including pesticides, herbicides, and pharmaceuticals. The top 3 per cent of all farms purchase 21 per cent of all fertilizers.[11] They are also the big users of common labor, hiring 35 per cent of all agricultural workers.[11] Eighty-five per cent of all farms that employ 10 or more regular laborers are in this exclusive bracket.[11] It has already been indicated that this group of 102,000 farms accounts for 31.5 per cent of all farm production. The number of elite and blue ribbon farmers is surprisingly small, but the concentration of so much of agriculture's resources and buying power in a group of such modest size gives its members an extraordinary influence in business and politics. Their wishes are listened to with more respect than those of any other segment of husbandry. What they consider to be their best interests almost automatically become the best interests of those who manufacture the things a farmer buys, whether they be trucks or hormones. The ties between big business, big agriculture, and big politics are often highly personal, just as in the time of Spanish settlement.

Not all farms in the exclusive $40,000-and-up class are extensive land operations; some utilize only a few acres and, in that sense, they are not haciendas. Nevertheless, in terms of aggregate capital resources they may be considered a modern species of this form of farm organization. In recent years the major capital resources of quite a number of agricultural enterprises have been concentrated in buildings and machinery rather than in land. This shift is in line with the contemporary belief that certain forms of intensive livestock husbandry can be more efficient than extensive types that depended primarily upon land in the days before power machinery. This is a distinctively American refinement of the Spanish concept of agricultural organization. The scale of operations, however, is reminiscent of the hacienda, and the hacienda is the father of this kind of enterprise, for it pioneered the way to efficient mass production.

A recent report by President Kennedy's 25-member Agricultural Advisory Commission indicates an awareness of the economic power of these new systems of husbandry in a field once associated almost exclusively with the small family farm. Declared the report in July 1962, "Scientists and engineers may go far in wiping out the physical possibility of the family farm through discovering profitable ways of separating the production of crops and livestock on the same farm throughout the Corn Belt and elsewhere. Should this happen, there probably would not be much left of family farming, as livestock feeding would be organized in an approximate factory process."[12] What the report might have added is that such a reorganization could not come about without a great concentration of capital in individual units. The hacienda has shown that such capital concentration is feasible. The technical problem left to "scientists and engineers" can easily be solved. There are already quite a few working models of feeding factories doing handsomely.

THE HACIENDA ADVANCES

The spread of vertical, capital-intensive types of operations is not impeded by a need to consolidate many small units of land into one large holding. In areas where land consolidation is difficult because of many small holdings the vertical, capital-intensive type of concentrated husbandry may be the solution for those with capital resources and a desire to move ahead rapidly. Such "vertical" haciendas have increased on the edges of big cities where prime markets are located, particularly on the Atlantic Coast between Boston and Washington. They are also multiplying in the corn belt, the Texas panhandle, and in western irrigated valleys. (Map 2.)* Where land is essential, as in the production of field crops or grass-fed livestock, the spread of the traditional land-intensive horizontal hacienda may be impeded by a predominance of smaller middle class farms. Consequently, while examples of the horizontal hacienda exist, this form of organization is not yet prominent in the Appalachian-Ozark mountain country, the Great Lakes dairyland, or the wheat belt. (Map 2.) It is more common in California, Florida, Texas and in the Mississippi Delta. It is noticeable in the Mountain states where extensive leases of public domain have been amalgamated with tracts of private irrigated pastures and haylands. The economic power of these large units is so convincingly demonstrated that as time goes on they will be observed more frequently in the areas once dominated by middle class commercial farms. It will take much time, however, for present owners to sell out and for others to consolidate little properties into larger ones.

The kind of farm program adopted in Washington from year to year understandably has great influence upon the rate at which agriculture's center of gravity shifts. The net effect of farm policy in recent years has been to weaken the small commercial farmer's position in the market place and to increase his disposition to close up shop and sell out. That government policy has had this complexion is largely due to the persuasive maneuvering of the hacienda at the highest political and administrative levels. In general hacienda operators, with their inside connections and more efficient techniques, have opposed restrictions upon production and marketing. They know that in free competition they can undersell the small operators and gain the upper hand in the market. Given

* Map 2 does not distinguish between the "land-intensive" and the "other capital-intensive" types.

another fifteen years of agricultural policy similar to that which has prevailed in the past, the hacienda will break what feeble economic strength still remains in the possession of the 1.3 million Lower Middle Class farms. There is no need to even consider the fate of the 1.6 million farms in the Third Class because their economic power has already been liquidated.

The advance of hacienda agriculture necessarily is somewhat restricted by its extraordinary capital requirements. As a rule, at least one-quarter of a million dollars in fixed capital is necessary for even "small" operations of this type. Only in part has the new capital needed for the extension of the hacienda system come from profits in farming. At times it has come from oil royalties and profits from the sale of land for urban real estate development. It is not surprising that such windfalls should be prime sources of capital for hacienda expansion when it is realized that major oil producing areas are in regions of early Spanish settlement, and that big cities in former Spanish territories often abut large ranches. When oil or real estate windfalls occur on large properties, really big capital becomes available for investment. Since tax advantages make agriculture an attractive field for investment, this money is often reinvested in land on an even grander scale. The possibility that oil may be found on agricultural properties bought with oil royalties is not overlooked.

Land sales prompted by the explosive growth of cities in the past two decades have made considerable capital available to some of the most capable agriculturists in the Southwest and in Florida. Most of this capital has remained at home but some of it has moved east and north where farms have been purchased on the fringes of more populous and faster growing cities. The ultimate aim may be further capital gains from land sales but while the property is being held for future real estate appreciation it may be developed agriculturally in hacienda fashion. If the investments are soundly made and advanced techniques are used, the agricultural operations themselves can be profitable. According to tax regulations the profits from sales of farms are not taxed at all if they are promptly reinvested in other agricultural lands or used in the development of such new lands. This tax advantage is a special incentive for agriculturists to reinvest profits from sales in similar enterprises.

Sunbelt interests by no means have a monopoly in the field of coordinated farm and real estate development. They have only set the style in a grand manner and shown what can be done with an initial advantage of inherited hacienda grants. Tens of thousands of middle class farmers all over the United States have also found themselves enriched by the sale of properties on the urban fringe, and have tended to reinvest their sudden wealth in larger agricultural holdings. Often, enough capital can be secured from the sale of 80 to 160 acres on the edge of an expanding city to purchase many hundreds of acres elsewhere and develop them to a far higher state of productivity than they have ever known before. This type of expansion is particularly noticeable in some of the better agricultural districts of the Midwest and along the urbanized Atlantic seaboard.

While the proportion of all farms which are struck by the happy lightning of oil and real estate wealth is small, they are nevertheless widely distributed and they have built up a productive capacity which gives them a considerable advantage in highly competitive markets. The profitability of these bigger, streamlined units tends to draw investment capital from outside of agriculture into similar operations. It makes the position of the ordinary middle class farmer, who has no hope of capital accumulation, even more desperate. To survive he has to pit expensive borrowed funds against cheap tax-salvaged wealth, and that is a tough assignment.

Chapter 4

Land and the Demand for Space

TOWNSMEN AND COUNTRYMEN

While a decline in the number of farms helps to thin the rural population and pack more people into cities, the expansion of cities tends to reverse the process and bring some people back close to the farm. This latter development has created problems for Carlos Meremonte, who operates a dairy farm on the rural-urban fringe of Greater St. Louis. It seems that herdsman Meremonte's gentle cattle, accustomed to more rustic ways, literally cannot stomach their existence on the city's doorstep. Even if proximity does present certain market advantages, these benefits are offset by a rising number of duffers at the neighboring Southmoor Country Club. Golfballs lofted over the Southmoor fence are eaten by the Meremonte cattle. This has led to gastrointestinal complications among what had been clover-loving animals, and farmer Meremonte has filed a petition for an injunction against the urbanites and their stray playthings.[1] He has sought through the wisdom of the courts to subdue this metropolitan encroachment upon the traditional rural way of bovine life. If this unhappy dairyman shares the fate

of other countrymen before him, the inexorable advance of the
city and its forward phalanx of sportsmen will not be blunted. As
humanity takes to the city to make a living, so it is prone to return
in leisure hours to the country, seeking pleasure in ways that may
be quite unpleasant for the farmer.

Some time ago when city hunter Merle Price of Des Moines,
Iowa complained to the Open Forum Editor of the *Sunday Register* that farmers seem overly hostile to hunters on their land, he
flushed a covey of sharp responses.[2] Among those inclined to re-
buttal was farmer H. E. Goebel, who gave the intrusive townsman
both barrels. "I don't know about the other farmers," wrote Mr.
Goebel, "but I for one will do anything to discourage these weekend killers from coming to my farm. I feel the wild animals and
birds that God and I allow to live on my land are almost as much
mine as are the cattle, sheep and hogs I raise and are for me to enjoy as I will. I like to see the mother quail hobble off in the summer, trying to make me think she is hurt so as to get me to chase
after her; in that way she may protect her young. I even like to
watch the skunk hunting mice in the alfalfa in the evening. I enjoy
watching the rabbits and squirrels scamper and play. I believe in
hunting and feel that without it our land might be overpopulated
with wild animals. But I also think that, if you cannot find some
other way to amuse yourself on weekends, you should buy a farm
and then you can tramp down the fences, leave the gates open,
drive into the fields, and in general make any sort of nuisance of
yourself you wish."

Another respondent, Mrs. Glenn Gravert, said her family might
welcome sportsmen in the hunting season if they would come
around with strong backs at harvest time. "I wonder if the hunter
would get more co-operation from the farmer if he would show
up during the summer and donate a little of his time?" inquired
Mrs. Gravert. "We are not against city hunters. Several parties (no
relation) have hunting privileges on our farm. They do show up
during the busy summer to lend a hand, and they really enjoy

themselves." Another farm wife, Mrs. Alfred Kendrick, also had a practical suggestion. "Twice in the past three seasons we've had a cow killed," she informed the editor. "I say if the state collects the license fees it should provide a place with game for the hunters and not turn them loose on the farmers." The Open Forum Editor realized, as his column ran out of space, that he had collided with a hot issue.

A farmer who would not have objected to a handful of hunters crossing his land two decades ago now feels he must post his property against the mobs that would park their cars along the highway and overrun his fences and fields. A farmer in Paris, Ontario was discouraged by the way hunters flaunted the No Trespassing sign on his property, so he replaced it with one which proclaimed: Trespassers Will Be Prosecuted. But the result was the same; the hunters ignored the sign and swarmed over his land. Now a new sign reads: Trespassers Will Be Shot. The gunners got the message and the farmer lives once more in rustic isolation. People who will not authorize their governments to buy public recreation grounds and set aside more of the public domain for the use of urban citizens, have no reason to complain about the measures farmers take to protect private lands, together with the crops and livestock which are their livelihood.

Perhaps neither urbanite nor farmer realizes how significantly increases in population and shifts in the patterns of settlement have altered forever the land requirements of town and country. In 1935 the farm population of the United States stood at an all-time high of 32 million.[3] Since, at that time, the entire population of the United States was 127 million, farmers were a substantial 25 per cent of the total. A quarter of a century is only a trivial fraction of historical time, yet today's picture is radically different. Now the farm population is down to 15 million[3] and farmers constitute only 8 per cent of a total population of 185 million. The great majority of Americans have begun to realize what it means to live without the "free" outdoors. Most of them no longer even have relatives on farms whom they can visit. Easy contact with the rural world is severed and urban people are cramped for space, particularly public space for recreation.

Agricultural interests both gain and lose by current shifts in population and changes in the uses of land. More people eat more food — that is a net gain in market for the farmer, especially in this era of surplus crops. Also, a net drop in the number of farms means that the bigger market is shared by fewer producers. However, the rising competition for land boosts the cost of farm property. Real estate values rose more than 300 per cent between 1935 and 1959[4] and the end is not yet in sight. Agriculture must inevitably pass on to the consumer the higher interest charges on its inflated property values. The city not only will pay for these inflated land values in the costs of its food, but it will also have to lay out increasingly larger sums for any farm land it purchases for expanded building, for water reservoir sites, and for open recreational areas. The American people who once reveled in their wealth of "wide-open spaces" are now caught in a land squeeze.

CONCENTRATION

The total acreage devoted to agriculture will probably decline slowly in the years ahead as other interests compete for land, but farmers will hold onto the biggest share of the nation's space as they have in the past. While the weak sell out, the strong will bid against each other to establish larger and more efficient holdings. In 1930 the average size of all farms was 157 acres.[4] By 1962 the average size had grown to 336 acres.[5] More significant than the increase in the average size of holding has been the tendency, during this period of transition, for farm land to become concentrated in the hands of a few operators. In 1930 there were 691,654 farmers who had 260 acres or more, and they controlled 54.9 per cent of all land in farms.[6] According to the most recent Census of Agriculture, the number of farmers with 260 acres or more has increased only slightly, to 812,625, but this group now has 76.3 per cent of all agricultural land.

The concentration of the great mass of farm acreage into larger units has been paralleled not only by a heavy drop-out of little farms but also by an inability to grow much on the part of those little farms which have survived. In 1930 there were over 5.6 million census farms with less than 260 acres. By 1959 there were 2.9 million census farms in this category and they averaged only 88 acres apiece. As the hacienda and other large agricultural units bid up the price of land and take the lion's share of it, it becomes even more unlikely that the small unit will survive except in those special cases where capital equipment is a substitute for land.

Farms of 1,000 acres and over possessed only 28 per cent of all agricultural land in 1930. By 1945 they held 40.3 per cent.[6] By 1959, at the time of the last Census of Agriculture, these big units, which are only 3.7 per cent of all farms, had garnered 49.2 per cent of the acreage. Their average size is now 4,045 acres." A major cause of the accelerated overproduction in agriculture has been the stepped-up concentration of land in the hands of a small number of well-financed, efficient operators who can get bigger yields from a given acreage by modern mass production methods. The shift of land from weak to strong management is one of the most significant agricultural developments of the past quarter century. It has completely deranged the economic basis of small-farm agriculture.

EFFICIENCY

In 1961 the Department of Agriculture published a report[7] on the comparative efficiency of cotton farms with high and low capital investments, in various parts of the South and Southwest. These data illustrate how farm efficiency improves with size and invested capital. The years covered by the study were 1957–59. Units with total average investments of $13,000 to $54,000 had net annual returns per acre which ranged from $4 to $14. Their yields of cotton

---

* This figure is much enlarged by the inclusion of ranches. In 1959 the average farm in First Class had 1,338 acres; the average Upper Middle Class farm had 445 acres; the average Lower Middle Class farm had 241 acres, and Third Class farms averaged 86 acres (Table 13).

varied from 204 pounds to 439 pounds per acre. The average size
of these farms was 58 to 404 acres and the area planted to cotton
varied from averages of 8 to 112 acres. By contrast, those farms
with total capital investments of $103,000 to $870,000 had net profits
that ranged from an average of $13 to an average of $92 per acre.
Yields of cotton ranged from 471 pounds to 1,040 pounds per acre.
The average size of these farms varied from 329 acres to 1,201
acres, and the amount of land planted to cotton averaged from 122
to 427 acres. The advantage enjoyed by a large, efficient hacienda
with a cotton allotment of 427 acres shows up clearly in the net income picture. According to the study, farms in this category averaged 1,201 acres of which 1,080 were cropland. Their over-all profit
per acre for every acre of the unit was $65. The poorest group of
little farms averaged 58 acres with 15 planted to cotton. The average profit earned on every acre in these units was $7. (See also Ta-
bles 3 and 10.)

It is obvious that a cotton allotment is far more productive under
hacienda management than it is in the hands of a submarginal
farmer. This is a major factor behind current efforts to persuade
the little farmer to put his land in the soil bank and let his cotton
allotment pass on to a bigger operator. Advocates of this policy
tell Congress that overproduction in agriculture is due to an over-
abundance of farmers, and that market supply and demand will
come into balance if only more small, inefficient operators drop
out of business. This is a curious argument in view of the facts
(Tables 3, 10).

One of the reasons that the operators of submarginal farms have
not moved out of agriculture is that alternative ways to make a
living in the city are uninviting. Many of these surplus people are
illiterate Negroes and whites who would have a hard time to find
employment, let alone social acceptance, elsewhere. Those who
have long claimed that greater efficiency in agriculture can be accomplished by persuading more small farmers to get out are abso-
lutely right. What these advocates of a streamlined agriculture

overlook is that the mounting surpluses produced by government-subsidized efficient farmers are not wanted now; neither is it desirable that more inefficient farmers be cast off to swell the rolls of the urban unemployed. To achieve a healthier agriculture at the expense of a sicker urban society is hardly a commendable alternative to the present situation.

TOO MANY FARMERS?

In July, 1962 efficient farms, paced by big-scale industrial agriculture, were sufficiently productive to convince Theodore O. Yntema, chairman of the finance committee of the Ford Motor Company, and other members of the Committee for Economic Development that the United States had committed too many of its resources to agriculture and would get along better with fewer farmers. The CED thought something should be done to encourage withdrawal of excess resources, so that the present oversupply of farm goods could be whittled down to demand and the taxpayer might be relieved of his obligations to support unnecessary production. "This is the heart of the matter in agricultural adjustment," announced a CED report.[8] "Excess resources in use in the production of farm goods *is* the farm problem."

The CED backed up its diagnosis with a chart which showed that between 1940 and 1960 investment in farm machinery and equipment had more than doubled, while purchases of fertilizer had quadrupled. During this same period, according to the chart, the amount of land in farms remained almost constant while manpower was about halved. What struck some readers of the report as illogical was the conclusion which the CED drew from its own statistics. Instead of associating overproduction with an overcommitment of technological resources, it attributed the excess mainly to an oversupply of people in farming.

The CED spotted the two problems of surplus production and surplus farmers — then, it concluded that the former proceeded from the latter. Only secondarily did it recognize that agriculture is overweight in capital investment. In a detailed plan designed to cut back supply to demand in a free market, the CED recommended: ". . . policies and programs to attract excess resources from use in farm production . . . ," to the end that the smaller total of resources at use in farm production will be composed of ". . . *a much smaller amount of labor and possibly, somewhat less of capital*."* Once this was accomplished, the CED could foresee a healthier farm scene: "Production per unit of resources used in agriculture will be higher . . . Earnings . . . will be higher, on the average, and these earnings will be obtained through sale of farm products without government subsidy or support."

If the CED had been historically minded, it would have been known that, in the past, the production of surpluses has increased as the commitment of labor resources has declined and the commitment of capital resources has increased. It should have been wary when it drew the conclusion that "Production per unit of resources used in agriculture will be higher . . . Earnings . . . will be higher, on the average, and these earnings will be obtained through sale of farm products without government subsidy or support." Any development which would make production and earnings higher per unit of investment would most certainly draw more capital into agriculture. This, in a period of surplus production sustained at the taxpayer's expense, is precisely the kind of stimulant agriculture does not need. At the moment agriculture is too efficient for the market to absorb its production. The result is an annual bill of around \$5 billion for subsidies which is delivered to the Treasury by the Department of Agriculture.

In the final analysis even the CED could not look a free market squarely in the eye. It proposed instead a five-year ". . . Temporary Income Protection Program" which would "prevent a sharp decline in farm incomes." Why fewer farmers producing more per unit of resources at greater profit should need any further income

* Italics not in original.

protection is not clear, especially as the support prices recommended by the CED would encourage rather than discourage the use of the most modern mass production techniques. In what it called its "Adaptive Approach" the CED recommended a plan of lower support prices for active farmers plus supplementary incentive payments to those willing to surrender their crop allotments and put their land in a soil bank. This is the same formula which in the 1950's promoted a heavy exodus of small farmers and stimulated capital investment and surplus production by big agriculture.

Unquestionably American agriculture would be more efficient if two million inefficient farmers were to drop out of the picture. It is perfectly clear also that efficient farmers, equipped with all the active acreage allotments, would have a field day growing surplus crops for the government at CED's "adjustment prices" of 22 cents a pound on cotton, $1.35 a bushel on wheat, and $1.00 a bushel on corn. It has long been apparent to those who know the costs of production of agricultural commodities on the most efficient farms that government price supports are extraordinarily high. Support prices based, not on the costs of efficient production, but on what inefficient operators require have been among the most compelling forces pulling fresh capital into agriculture from outside sources. In 1961 the government support price on cotton was 31 cents a pound, that on wheat $1.78 a bushel, and that on corn, $1.20. These prices were roughly double the costs of production by efficient mass production farmers.* The profits of the latter have been in almost direct proportion to the amount of land they could put under the plow. It is this condition which has helped to boost real estate values and promote the concentration of land holdings into a few strong hands.

* In October, 1962, *Progressive Farmer* reported on the prices at which cotton growers in different parts of the United States would quit growing the crop. In the old-time stronghold of the Carolina piedmont the drop-outs would generally begin at 30 cents a pound and the area would close down at 25 cents. In the new, irrigated cotton section of the Texas High Plains the drop-outs would begin at 16 cents and the area would shut down at 13 cents.

To trim federal price supports by 20 to 25 per cent would only tend to clear the field faster of inefficient farmers and leave the subsidized government market wide open to mass producers who could sustain their present levels by buying more machinery, more fertilizers, and more acreage. Instead of reducing the total resource commitment in agriculture, such a policy as CED recommended would only cut the number of farmers while it would stimulate an increased capital commitment.

That big agriculture in particular thrives at government price support levels was amply demonstrated by data supplied to Congress by Representative Lindley Beckworth of Texas on June 18, 1962. According to Representative Beckworth's statistics a group of 296 high-speed cotton growers took over $30 million in government price support loans on their 1960 crops — an average of $100,000 each. Eighty individual cotton farmers received government support loans ranging from $103,186 to $733,256; many more received between $50,000 and $100,000.[9] The largest government price support loan on cotton granted to a single producer in 1960 was for $1,236,048. This payment went to the Delta & Pine Land Co. of Scott, Mississippi which also qualified as a corn farmer and collected $11,409 from the government for reducing its corn acreage. In August, 1962 Delaware's Honorable John J. Williams had a few words to say to his colleagues about Delta & Pine's government payments: "This operation is not even owned by Americans; it is owned by the Fine Spinners & Doubles, Ltd., of Manchester, England. Just how a British corporation in Manchester, England, owning land in America, could qualify as an American farmer eligible for subsidy payments, is something only the imagination of a New Frontiersman could comprehend."[10] Republican Senator Williams was, of course, excused by his colleagues for not mentioning in an election year that quite a few Republicans had voted for the farm program that made these payments possible.

Not all cotton growers fared as well under the government price support program as the efficient operators cited by Representative

Beckworth. Between the 1949 and 1959 censuses of agriculture the total number of cotton growers dropped from 1,110,000 to 509,000 — a reduction of over 50 per cent in the number of small inefficient operators. The ranks of the big operators increased from 38,000 to 54,000 between 1950 and 1959. (Table 4.)

There could be only two valid reasons for using public funds to encourage inefficient farmers to move out of agriculture. One would be if the country were short of food and needed to put its lands in more expert hands. This is obviously not the case now although as the population increases the situation may change. The other would be if agriculture's surplus manpower were needed elsewhere. Considering the high rate of urban unemployment that has persisted in recent years it would seem that the market for unskilled labor is already oversupplied. Until the nation needs their lands and labor, inefficient farmers may be better off where they are than if they were to head for the city's slums and welfare rolls.

A small potato grower in Maine who had run out of credit and was about to quit farming sized up his own predicament this way: "Will I and my family," he asked, "make better citizens in some city slum than if we could have stayed here on the farm? I have six children. Here each one has chores to do. They get a good schooling and at home they develop a sense of responsibility. What will they do in the city where I can't afford to rent a decent house in a decent neighborhood? I figure the city has enough problems without turning six good kids into more juvenile delinquents."

TOO MUCH LAND?

If it is true, as the CED data seem to indicate, that the overcommitment of resources to agriculture lies more in the direction of capital investment than in the direction of labor, it would be well to take a look at the nation's total land resource and how it is used. In the last analysis land is the most important of agriculture's capital resources. Land represents 70 per cent of the total value of all farm real estate and this real estate in 1960 was worth $129.1 billion. By comparison, all other farm property, including livestock and machinery, had a combined value of only $34.6 billion in 1960.[11] Land is definitely the key capital resource of agriculture.

The extraordinary competition for the lands vacated by those forced to withdraw from agriculture in the past two decades is one of the remarkable anomalies of our time. Agriculture received unique taxpayer subsidies out of cries that it was nearly bankrupt, yet every year land, its primary asset, enjoyed a marked increase in value. According to the time-honored principle that a bull market indicates strength, it would seem that agriculture never before had it so good. Successful farmers have shown that greater capital commitments in land are good investments. The result may be overproduction, but as long as the government buys surpluses the game is very profitable for the efficient operator.

LAND FOR AGRICULTURE

It has been noted previously that 58.9 per cent of the area of the 48 contiguous states is in farms.* In addition to this land, another 48 million acres of private property and 287 million acres of the public domain are used for grazing. These 335 million acres are 17.6 per cent of the 48 contiguous states. Thus the space devoted to agriculture and livestock husbandry totals 76.5 per cent of the landscape of those states.[12] The grazing lands of the public domain, which are 15.1 per cent of the area, have a very low produc-

---

* In the following discussion the data for Alaska and Hawaii are often omitted. Because Alaska and Hawaii were so recently admitted to statehood historical statistics on changes in land utilization for the 50 states are not satisfactory. Until such statistics do become available, detailed consideration of important historical trends in land utilization must be confined to the 48 contiguous states. However, statistics for Hawaii and Alaska would not greatly alter the total picture of agricultural land use because all private lands in both states amount to less than 10 million acres out of a total of 370 million acres. Because 97.6 per cent of Alaska is federal or state property, at the moment it seems best not to include its vast land mass in every current statistical assessment. The omission of Hawaii is not of great consequence in presenting the total national picture because Hawaii's total area is less than 4 million acres. The land area of the 48 contiguous states is 1,902 million acres. The land area of the 50 states is 2,271 million acres. (See Table 6.)

tive capacity. Nevertheless, to the extent that this government property furnishes animal feeds which otherwise would not be available to stockmen, it contributes to surplus feed production. At the same time that the federal government pays out millions of dollars annually to put private lands in the soil bank, the Department of Agriculture and the Department of the Interior, as custodians of the public domain, lease lands for grazing at bargain-basement rates. As recently recorded in the *Congressional Record*,[13] private landowners received $3.00 for carrying one cow one month in the same district where the federal government practically gave away similar privileges for 22 to 49 cents.* This is only one of many similar examples of how public policies, for lack of coordination, work at cross-purposes to defeat each other's objectives — a condition which costs the taxpayer dearly.

From time to time the House of Representatives calls upon the federal government's General Accounting Office to report on how the taxpayers' money is spent. Recently the House Appropriations Subcommittee was startled to learn that the Department of Agriculture had paid farmers in New Mexico and Colorado from $1.94 to $12.00 an acre a year to put leased public lands in the Soil Bank Reserve. In one instance in New Mexico the General Accounting Office investigators found "about 550 acres leased [from the state] for 25 cents an acre was placed in the Reserve at an annual rental rate of $9.00 an acre." When questioned, Agriculture Department officials told House investigators the procedure is legal.[14]

In 1960 the government leased 141 million acres of range lands in Federal Grazing Districts to 18,371 operators — an average of about 7,600 acres (almost 12 square miles) to each rancher. In Nevada, which is about 85 per cent public domain, over 42 million acres of federal lands were leased to 974 operators — an average of 43,000 acres (67 square miles) apiece. (If the whole state of Con-

* Western range lands are usually rented, not by the acre, but by the Animal-Unit-Month. One A.U.M. is the amount of land required to carry one cow for one month.

necticut were divided into chunks of 43,000 acres, there would be enough land for 74 farmers.) For renting 180 million acres of the public domain in 1961 the Bureau of Land Management charged only $2,764,863, or less than two cents an acre.[15]

In 1960 the Bureau of Land Management leased 17 million acres of better quality "Taylor Act" grazing lands to 9,645 permittees for about 18 cents an acre. As reported in the *Congressional Record* of March 1, 1962 the "Receipts from BLM [Bureau of Land Management] grazing fees in Taylor Act districts brought in $3 million in 1960. In this fiscal year of 1962 we will spend more than $4 million for range management and protection alone, plus nearly a million for weed control and a large part of the $6.5 million allocated to soil and moisture conservation on public lands." If full commercial rates were charged for the use of Taylor Act lands these properties would return a substantial profit to the taxpayer. As it is, under present BLM management, it is a heavy expense to the public to rent its own property.

Now the BLM has grand notions of what should be done to improve the lands under its jurisdiction. It has a fifty-year public program which is called "Project Twenty-Twelve" because it will run from 1962 to the year 2012. Under this plan[16] the BLM expects to step up the rate of range reseeding to 434,000 acres a year by 1965. It intends to fence in public property for the convenience of private lessees at the rate of 3,645 miles annually by 1980. At this rate enough fence would be built each year to cross the continent. In 1961 the BLM was killing sagebrush at the rate of 132,000 acres annually at a cost of $3 an acre.[16] By the year 2012 it expects to have controlled sagebrush on 32 million acres.

Quite clearly the spending program is going to increase in intensity if BLM has its way, but in the prospectus for "Project Twenty-Twelve," nothing is said about raising grazing fees to parity with those charged on private property. All of the expenditures projected by the BLM will go to subsidize fewer than 30,000 ranchers,[17] only a fraction of whom would function if they were obliged to compete with other farmers on a free enterprise basis. The most ironical feature of this expensive subsidization is that it keeps domestic livestock on land that would otherwise support more wild game and be available for public recreation for urban populations which are short of recreational space. Whenever it is suggested that certain areas of the public domain be converted to park and wildlife reservations the most vociferous opposition comes from the very livestockmen who have so long been subsidized by the welfare state.

In 1961 when the federal government proposed to take one-third of a million acres of grazing lands in southeastern Utah and convert them into a Canyonlands National Park, the state's governor, George Dewey Clyde, let it be known that any plans for a new national park "will be opposed to the last ditch" if they should threaten the livestock industry.[18] Governor Clyde and livestockmen were still resentful of the fact that some public grazing lands had been withdrawn from general use to compensate Navajo tribes for lands they had surrendered for park purposes at Glen Canyon Dam. Governor Clyde in the summer of 1961 said that transferring the remaining good public grazing lands in the country to compensate for any other park withdrawals of Navajo land "must be vigorously opposed."[18]

Both government officials and the lessees of federal lands contend that if grazing were not permitted on the public domain at give-away prices, usable natural forage would be wasted. They say only those who are on the spot can utilize it. When the government rents private property at commercial rates to put it in the soil bank, grazing is prohibited and forage is wasted. In the case of the soil bank, however, government officials and landowners argue that the unused forage is desirable for wildlife and as a soil builder which retards erosion and prevents excessive water run-off. Whatever side the taxpayer chooses to take in the debate over what is wasted forage and what is soil conservation, it appears that he cannot win. What is good for the soil on private lands apparently is not good for the soil on public lands; what is wasted forage on public lands is not wasted forage on private lands. This kind of reasoning costs the taxpayer heavily.

SPORTSMEN

Sportsmen, campers, and tourists have taken a more active interest in the public domain than citizens at large. Through their spokesmen they have expressed the opinion that more government lands should be reserved for wildlife and recreation. They claim that if those livestock operators who cannot afford to pay going commercial rates were denied access to the public domain then wildlife, particularly antelope, deer, and elk, would become more plentiful all over the mountain West, to the greater enjoyment of those who hunt and those who simply like to see native animals in their natural habitat. These "dudes" and their notion that public lands should be for public use are not popular in inefficient, subsidized livestock circles.

In 1960 it was estimated by the Bureau of Land Management[19] that of all the forage available on 141 million acres of range only 11 per cent was available to wildlife; the rest was monopolized by cattle and sheep. However, the total supply of grass on these 141 million acres was only enough for 1.3 million head of cattle or their equivalent in sheep. About 3.9 million cattle or their equivalent in sheep actually go onto the range, but they are there for only about one-third of the year since the average grazing season on BLM land is about 4 months. The total beef cattle population of the United States was 67 million in 1961. If 2 per cent of U.S. beef cattle or their equivalent in sheep were excluded from the public range, the quantity of feed available to big game would be increased 9 times.

In the eleven years between 1950 and 1961 the number of recreational visits to National Forests jumped from 27 million to 102 million. Attendance at National Forests now overshadows attendance at National Parks, many of which have become so crowded that they offer little real sense of wilderness. In 1950 the visits made to National Parks totaled 33 million. A decade later patronage zoomed to 79 million. The National Parks have an area of only 25 million acres while there are 185 million acres in National Forests. These forest lands, which have 81,000 miles of fishing streams and 2 million acres of lakes, are now the Mecca of those who seek the truly wild outdoors. Some of the National Forests are equipped with facilities for sportsmen and campers, but these places are not the most popular. Of the millions of visits made to National Forests in 1960 only one-third were to the "improved" spots; the rest were to places where people could be on their own without any reminders of civilization.[20]

As the population of the United States becomes more urbanized, the attraction of both the National Parks and the National Forests becomes more compelling. The use of these public lands has sky rocketed at a rate many times that of population increase. It seems that confinement in cities and suburbs has imbued people with a greater desire to find occasional release in America's great outdoors. Fortunately this new interest in the public domain comes at a time when agriculture finds itself overextended in commitments to land resources and capable of raising bigger crops and more livestock on smaller acreages at greater profit. The reassignment of land from old uses to new ones which fit the needs of a fast growing urban society promises to be one of the most critical problems of resource allocation in the future. There is no better place for the government to respond to changes in the needs of the people and of the national economy than in the administration of federal public lands which are 21 per cent of the 48 contiguous states and 34 per cent of the entire 50 states. (Table 6.)

Public lands will not be put to new uses without objection. Livestock and lumber interests, having grown accustomed to the purchase of bargain grass and timber leases, may not gracefully switch over to the more expensive and competitive private economy. In 1962 the United States Senate tried to introduce some new thought into the management of the public domain through legislation to set aside 14 million acres of scenic wilderness exclusively for recreational use. However, the House Interior Subcommittee balked. According to one Washington source, reported in the *Morning News* of Wilmington: ". . . the subcommitte proposal would give miners, cattlemen, and lumbermen an even greater access to areas to be preserved than they now enjoy."[21] Added the *News:* "Various commercial interests in the western parts of the United States are strongly opposed to the Senate's wilderness bill."

Even while the Senate and House were deliberating over what to do about preserving this 8 per cent of the National Forests in a virgin state, the U. S. Forest Service decided to open up one of its wilderness areas under a "landscape management" plan. David Brower, executive director of the Sierra Club of San Francisco, made some comments about this which Congressman John D. Dingell inserted in the *Congressional Record*.[22] "Where is the de facto wilderness going, going?" asked Mr. Brower. Then he replied, "The question seems almost academic, like asking where are the dodo and passenger pigeon and all the other 20,000 or so extinct wild things going, going? . . . Where does it go, for example, when the Forest Service decides, as it did last week, that Waldo Lake should join a newly named class and become a landscape management area? From what I have read in the Forest Service March 30 release about this landscape management area idea, it is just warmed-over Deadman Summit, where some national forest just southeast of Yosemite contained one of the most beautiful stands of virgin Jeffery pine you ever saw . . . recreation was judged to be predominant. But the logs came out just the same . . ."

COMPETITION FOR LAND

In October, 1962 President Kennedy signed a bill which authorizes the Department of Interior to acquire midwestern wetlands for migratory waterfowl.[23] This laudable conservation act might have raised no eyebrows had it not been clear to all concerned that the reason government monies were needed to buy public swamps for ducks was that other government monies had been appropriated to drain private marshy farm lands — this so their operators could raise crops for which even more government cash would be paid, sometimes to the same operators already being paid not to raise those same crops on land already well drained. If this sequence is hard to follow the reader should not be demoralized. Even Congress, expert as it is at creating involved subsidy chains, often gets lost in its own tracks.

During the ceremony at the signing of the wetlands bill the inconsistency of competing government programs piled one upon the other became clear to a number of participants including the President, who laughed and said that the bill would enable the Department of the Interior to acquire wetlands before the Department of Agriculture could pay farmers to drain them. Just why the Department of Agriculture should be paying farmers to drain swamps to raise more wheat and corn at a time when it is also paying them to raise less wheat and corn was not discussed.

Chapter 5

Debate and Decision

Even if we accept the loose definition of a farm used by the Census of Agriculture, there were only 15 million persons living on farms in 1959. Since that year the estimated drop-out rate has averaged 4 per cent a year.[1] Such high mortality gives survivors the jitters. It is no wonder they are agitated and prone to grab in all directions for straws. A lot of people who are in line for elimination do not want to quit farming. They are being squeezed out by a combination of technology, economics, and politics which they can do very little to resist if they lack the capital to expand and take full advantage of new techniques, tax loopholes, and government subsidies. Fellow farmers, professional farm spokesmen, professors, journalists, congressmen, bankers, merchants, physicians, labor organizers, and industrialists all have a straw or two of advice to toss to the farmer who is drowning in a sea of surplus crops and surplus wisdom.

As might be expected, farmers do not always take kindly to the advice which is proffered them. When the Committee for Eco-

nomic Development hit the nation's headlines with its finding that
American agriculture would be better off with lower price supports, no acreage controls, and two million fewer farmers,[2] the
Farmers Union Grain Terminal Association took radio time to
return the compliment. ". . . perhaps," said the broadcast for the
Association, "it would be only fair for farmers to try to . . . make
a report on what they'd recommend for corporations. Things, perhaps, like doing away with subsidies to big business, cutting tractor prices by a third, lowering interest rates one-half, unlocking
interlocking boards of directors, putting business on the free market so it could be competitive at home and around the world. In
other words, if corporation chiefs claim to know what's best for
farmers, we're sure farmers have some appropriate suggestions as
to what would be good for corporations." The broadcast ended
with a question: "What do you think?"

It did not take long for a few thoughts to materialize. In several
midwestern towns Ford dealers and Sears, Roebuck stores were
picketed by members of the National Farmers Organization because executives of these companies had served on the CED agricultural committee. Oren Lee Staley, national president of the
NFO, said the demonstrations were intended to get the companies
to repudiate the CED report.[3] Farmers, he implied, had had
enough free advice from outsiders to last them a while.

On the other hand the embattled husbandmen seem to be oblivi-
ous to the attitudes of a lot of people who are not "corporation
executives." Ordinary citizens have grown tired of giving up a
portion of their wages to support farm programs that only result
in more surpluses and bigger storage bills. Thirty years of subsidized farm surpluses have exhausted the public's tolerance for
"temporary" farm relief which seems to have bedded down into a
permanent slot in the budget.

In the late winter of 1962 Senator Kenneth B. Keating of New
York read to his colleagues a letter from a constituent which pretty
well summarized the feelings of harassed taxpayers.[4] "This morn-

ing," the constituent wrote, "I heard on the news broadcast as I was dressing to come to work that the farmers of this country received aid to the tune of $2½ billion last year. While I do not begrudge the poor farmer a bit of assistance, it means that out of the miserable pittance ($67 a week) that I earn, it costs me close to $10 a week in income taxes to the Federal Government. Out of this miserable pittance must come rent, telephone, gas and electricity bills, food and clothes. After all, I also am claiming the right to be classified as a human being. I'd like being subsidized myself. I realize that $2½ billion must seem like small change to you by this time. When am I as a plain common ordinary citizen of this country going to get some aid? Honestly, Senator, I need it."

The Senator's first comment on the letter was: "I would correct these sentiments only to say that the administration spent $4.7 billion on farm price supports last year, not $2.5 billion."

WHO GETS THE HELP?

The day has drawn to a close when farmers could count on broad public support for a program of government spending either to increase their profit margins when they are adequately capitalized or to keep them in full-time agriculture when they are undercapitalized. The fact that most of the help goes to a relatively small percentage of upper-bracket operators who are better off than the majority of taxpayers has hurt the cause of those who are really in a bind. As the farmers' ranks are thinned each year, the subsidies paid to those who remain increase rather than decrease. This fact does not make sense to the ordinary citizen who pays the bill. He would expect that fewer and more substantial farmers would need less help.

It should be emphasized that most agricultural commodities are not on the subsidy list (Table 14); public aid has been concentrated in certain selected segments of agriculture where overproduction is critical. In 1960 five commodities — cotton, wheat, corn, grain sorghums, and dairy products — received 91 per cent of all price support aid, yet they represented only 40 per cent of the value of all farm production. The producers of these commodities, however, are numerous, and they are heavily concentrated in the Lower Middle Class distress group. (Table 3.)

As much as 85 per cent of all corn is fed to livestock on the farm where it is grown or on farms nearby. Farmers themselves are the primary market for this feed grain. Thus, in this case, the public subsidizes a crop that is used primarily by the growers themselves. The peculiar character of the market for feed grains was discussed by Senator Spessard L. Holland of Florida during a congressional debate on the Food and Agriculture Act of 1962. Said the Senator: ". . . Some people see no difference between feed grains which are fed — 85 percent of them — either on the farm where they are produced, or nearby, and do not enter into the commercial handling of grains, and, on the other hand, tobacco, cotton, or rice, which certainly are not consumed on the farm. It is idle to put them in the same category because they are not. Mr. President, when we talk that way, we have our tongues in our cheeks, because we know perfectly well that the feed grains are consumed, in the main, on the farms where they are produced or in the nearby areas."[5]

INFLUENCE

Despite the decline in the number of farmers and the decline in rural populations, agricultural interests have long managed to maintain their influence in the nation's legislative halls. They have been able to do this because election districts in many cases did not reflect the new patterns of population settlement. Until very recently the rural districts of Maryland were able to elect a majority of the state senate, even though they contained less than 15 per cent of the state's population. Before 1962 one vote in Georgia's least populous county had a value equal to 100 votes in its most populous county. The late Governor Eugene Talmadge of Georgia was so contemptuous of the urban vote that he once declared he did not bother to campaign in counties where streetcars ran. In 1962

Vermont's state senatorial districts were the same as they had been in 1793 with the result that the Town of Burlington (population 33,000) had one state senator to match one senator from the Town of Victory (population 48). The same story of disproportionate legislative influence in the grip of rural minorities has characterized every state in varying degrees since the time when people in metropolitan areas began to outnumber those in rural districts back in the early 1920's.

In Mississippi, where there had been no reapportionment for seventy-two years, the legislature became deadlocked when it was called upon in 1962 to consider the issue. Rural legislators, who had exercised control since 1890, made a last ditch fight to set up a senate with one senator from each of the state's eighty-two counties. This idea was pushed by the local Farm Bureau Federation in the hope that it might preserve many agricultural tax exemptions since only ten counties in the state are considered urban.¹ Alabama tried a similar plan but it was overruled by a three-judge Federal Court. The manner in which the national Congress has voted generous subsidies for the farmer without demanding strict curtailment of production would be incomprehensible if the system of representation on the federal level had not also been stacked in agriculture's favor throughout the thirty years that the Treasury has been mailing checks to the folks back home.

Now it appears that the era of strong rural influence at the political pork barrel is near its end. In March, 1962 the U. S. Supreme Court indicated that election districts with greatly differing populations may violate the rights of individual citizens in the more populous districts by diluting the value of their ballots. Since that decision rural districts with small populations but strong legislative powers have begun to pull in their horns. It might be noted that in 1962 when Georgia held its first statewide popular vote primary for the governorship in fifty-four years, the urban candidate, Carl E. Sanders, trounced the incumbent, Marvin Griffin, whose strength lay in rural areas and who had been considered unbeata-

ble under the county unit system. When congressional reapportionment catches up with voter sentiment, as it will before many
Novembers, the dilapidated fence around the Treasury's green
clover patch will be mended by irate urbanites. Twenty-five years
ago farm residents were 24 per cent of the population.[8] Today they
are 8 per cent, and by 1980 they will be about 2 per cent.

THE LINE-UP

The consistency with which rural and urban interests may op-
pose one another on clear-cut issues was demonstrated when votes
were taken on the administration's separate bills for agriculture
and urban affairs in 1962. This was the first time that urban parti-
sans made a strong bid for a department of cabinet status. It came
on the 100th anniversary of the establishment of the Department
of Agriculture and failed partly because of rural objection. If both
of the administration's bills had passed there would have been less
federal spending on farms and more on cities. In the end the
House killed both bills. The Senate rejected a Department of Urban Affairs 58 to 42 while it approved the farm bill 42 to 38.[9] However, these summary tallies of the Senate's action are not the most
revealing measure of its sentiment, which was marked by a pro-
nounced division of sympathy along rural-urban lines. Sixty-seven
senators out of 100 consistently stood on one side or the other. Only
33 senators were flexible and either opposed both interests, favored
both, or did not vote on both issues.

The farm bill called for drastic controls which would have limited production to actual needs in return for federal price support.[9]
Agriculture's expansionists claimed this bill would be "hard" on
farmers. By contrast the urban affairs bill was commonly said to
be the forerunner of "easy" federal aid to the city. Thirty-six senators voted against both bills — a stand that favored federal money
for the farm but not for the city. Thirty-one senators reciprocated
by voting for both bills — a position that favored a boost in city
spending and a cut in farm outlays. The consistency of these 67

senators who voted to be "hard" on one side and "soft" on the other underscores the reality of the rural-urban split.

The increasing antagonism toward farm subsidies on the part of urban taxpayers seems to stem from the fact that Washington's farm spending, which began as a temporary relief appropriation, has become the third largest regular item in the federal budget where it follows defense and interest on the debt. Moreover, the farm program is no longer primarily a relief measure for the distressed, but has become instead an income subsidy device for one of the most progressive segments of the national economy. The financial distress of American agriculture, as it has been publicized in recent years, is largely a fiction evolved by lumping statistics and manipulating definitions in such a way as to make it appear that the plight of farmers in the lower brackets is the plight of all.

With 78 per cent of all farm income going to 22 per cent of the census farmers (Table 1) it is fairly obvious that these 22 per cent are the real producers and doing very well. The other 78 per cent of census farmers are no longer agriculturists in the modern sense and are not equipped to survive over the long haul unless drastic measures are taken soon to allocate to those who still have a chance a definite percentage of the market before their present percentage slips even more. Yearly doles will not do the trick; they just prolong the agony. If 78 per cent of all census farmers are doing badly it is not because the city is cheating them or the government is callous. It is because they are economically obsolete. A minority of progressive, high-speed agriculturists have pushed them to the wall and taken over the lion's share of production. The taxpayer is in no position to reverse what business competition has already achieved. There are other more critical social problems than this one calling for public attention — urban unemployment for one. The 0.8 million First Class and Upper Middle Class commercial farmers, who were defined in Chapter 2, and who produce most of the surpluses and consequently get the biggest government checks, are among the most successful of all American entrepreneurs. (Table 1.)

Those farmers who appear most distressed in the census data are helped very little by government programs. The 1.6 million Third Class operators, who are 44 per cent of all census farmers but take in only 5 per cent of all farm income (Table 1), are financially and physically incapable of producing surpluses. Their farms are not big enough, nor are they equipped with the machinery that would make overproduction possible. Their misery, which in some cases is real but more often contrived, makes all agriculture look sick. By a kind of mathematical editing, which seldom takes into account off-farm incomes that usually exceed farm incomes, these people are made to appear destitute.

THE BASIC CONFLICT

In between the 0.8 million farmers who constitute the prosperous and highly productive upper crust of American agriculture and that mass of 1.6 million part-time yeomen at the bottom, there are 1.3 million Lower Middle Class farmers many of whom are in full-time commercial agriculture and want to stay there. They think they can survive even though their chances are poor because by modern standards they are only semi-employed. They do not seem to realize that their basic trouble is that they have been out-flanked in economic competition by other farmers. Many of these Lower Middle Class farmers want to grow bigger. Others, realizing that capital is hard to come by, would like to be frozen in their present positions and figure that tight government controls through allotments could protect them against further encroachment by the hacienda and "adequate" family farms. Their competition argues against such a static, hold-the-line philosophy. It says this would stop technological advance and oblige the consumer to patronize inefficiency — a burden that could become as costly as present government programs.

It is up to the taxpaying public to choose whatever side it wishes in this basic conflict between efficient, well-capitalized farmers and those who are less efficient largely because they lack the capital to apply modern technology. If the public chooses to protect weak farmers by means of stringent government allotments, it will in effect underwrite inefficiency and in the end it might be penalized in the form of higher food prices. The magnitude of this risk is not great, however, since all 2.9 million farmers in the Lower Middle and Third Classes put together now have only 28 per cent of the market. As the NFO clearly demonstrated in the strike that failed, it takes more than the output of 28 per cent of the market to fix prices. Without government floor prices market levels are likely to be determined chiefly by what the 0.8 million farmers in the First and Upper Middle Classes will accept. As long as these producers, who account for 72 per cent of all production, operate competitively prices will be low.

The cost of food could only become unreasonable if, in addition to government allotments, the public were to continue to grant price supports as it has in the past. The history of price support efforts indicates that they do not shelter the small farmer, but they do stimulate his bigger competitors. They should be discontinued in favor of letting free enterprise determine price. As a concession to the marginal farmer, he should be offered the option to accept or reject an official allotment which would preserve for him his present small share of the market. He would not be well off and his lot would not be likely to improve, but he would not be so quickly forced out of business if he wanted to stay under the adverse circumstances he is already familiar with.

The sharp conflict of interests within the agricultural fraternity has become fairly transparent, and it is equally clear that public subsidies have aggravated it. There are three main types of public policy which might be advocated under the circumstances. One solution would be to withdraw all forms of government intervention and let farmers slug it out among themselves in a free market until only the fittest survive. Another solution would be to freeze the *status quo* with tight allotments. A third approach would be some kind of subsidy-sweetened compromise between these two extremes. A spirit of compromise has dominated Congress for the past thirty years. In its solicitude to hurt no farmer's feelings it has advanced and financed programs which have only feinted at the problem but never struck a solid punch. While this approach has been easy on agriculture it has been rough on the taxpayer. Costs to the public have mounted while farmers appear to be more displeased than gratified by the inconclusive results.

THE DILEMMA OF THE LOWER MIDDLE CLASS

Which way should farmers of the Lower Middle Class turn on farm policy — toward the free market or toward allotment controls? Or should they get out of agriculture altogether? In public opinion polls these farmers generally say they are opposed to government acreage allotments even with price supports. They still seem to cherish the dream that they will grow and catch up with "adequate" family farms. Yet in secret balloting these underdogs usually play it safe and approve controls.

While polls and ballots are not taken or recorded according to economic class, it is obvious from the small number of husbandmen in the top categories and the large number in the lower income groups that the latter can roll up a substantial majority on any issue put to a vote. Whenever all farmers vote it is the opinion of the low income groups which ultimately tips the scales, for these groups can cast more than two-thirds of the ballots even though they control less than one-third of agriculture's capacity to produce. Big agriculture's lobbies work hard in Congress, principally through the Farm Bureau, to prevent some crucial policy decisions from ever reaching the grass roots ballot box. In 1962 the administration under Secretary Freeman proposed that farmers producing the major surpluses of wheat, feed grains, and dairy products should be given a chance to decide between tight allotments with price supports and a free market without public aid. Only wheat farmers got the chance to vote and they approved the plan by a 68.4 per cent majority.[11]

A DIFFERENT OPINION

In April, 1962 Representative Silvio O. Conte of Massachusetts presented to Congress the summarization of a poll taken among farmers across the nation by *Farm Journal* which resulted in a different conclusion.[10] "Farmers may disagree about what they do want in the way of a farm policy," said the *Journal*, "but they're mighty clear about what they don't want." Added the pollsters, "They don't want compulsory government quotas. They don't want the Government running the farms of the country. They don't want the Secretary of Agriculture telling them how much, or how little, they can raise and sell without being whacked by a Government penalty." The *Farm Journal* did not claim infallibility but it thought it was on the right track. *"Farm Journal* makes no claim that such a poll shows anything with exactitude. We do say that it is a highly significant straw in the wind to show the direction of farm thinking. We believe it most certainly does that. Furthermore it cuts across all party and organizational lines. If we were a Congressman, a Senator, a Secretary of Agriculture or a President, we would pay serious attention to it."

The poll offered farmers three choices and they were asked to state a preference:

(1) Compulsory Government quotas on what I could sell, or how much I could farm; stiff penalties, support prices at, or above, present levels.

(2) Expanded voluntary land-retirement program to cut crop production; no compulsory quotas or allotments; with supports on crops at a level to stabilize markets but not add to surpluses.

(3) Get the Government clear out — no controls, no price supports.

The result was an impressive 52 per cent vote for No. 3 calling for the government to drop all farm controls and supports so as to let the free market forces of supply and demand take over. An almost negligible 4 per cent preferred No. 1, which was the administration's 1962 program for "managed abundance" through allotments, high supports, and penalties for non-compliance. Forty-four per cent favored No. 2, the road to voluntary land retirement and low price supports which would not add to surpluses.[10] If farmers were to vote 52 per cent for choice No. 3 in a real referendum on farm policy the taxpayer's worries would be over. Taking the government "clear out" of agriculture would ease federal spending mightily.

It is obvious from this contradiction between its philosophy and its actual performance in a real showdown vote that the Lower Middle Class wishes it could succeed by really trying in a competitive market, but confesses its inability to stand up to the stress that genuine competition would impose. Soon it will have to make up its mind as to what it wants in realistic terms, and assert that decision unequivocally or the initiative will pass to the city taxpayer who is growing impatient.

THE EXCLUDED TAXPAYER

In nearly every debate on farm policy which is conducted among farmers there is a blissful inclination to overlook the fact that some very interested bystanders would also like to be heard — the urban taxpayers who are obligated for the bill and who are compelled by the Internal Revenue Service to come up with the cash. If the farmer thinks the Department of Agriculture might be dictatorial, he should consider how the Treasury takes its cut out of the wage-earner's pay check before he even gets it. This brand of heavy-handed government control is relatively unfamiliar to the freedom-loving farmer who makes his own declaration of income.

The Treasury reported in the spring of 1962 that farmers fail to declare income of $4 billion a year which if taxed would yield $1½ billion to the public till.[12] If this fact were generally taken into account in official calculations of total net farm income, the financial status of agriculture in the record books would improve by about one-third. Farmers are not entirely to blame for their carelessness, however, for a solicitous Congress has given them a number of tax concessions and defended them against harsh criticism from the Treasury. Remarked one member of the House when the Internal Revenue Service made its report of the missing $4 billion: "... Mortimer Caplin's [the Commissioner of Internal Revenue's] charge that the American farmer fails to report an estimated $4 billion a year in taxable income is a shocking example of irresponsibility. ... The American farmer is becoming accustomed to taking it on the chin from the Federal Government, but is there no limit?"[12] The congressman concluded his remarks by suggesting an apology. "Again the heavy hand of Government is trying to coerce or intimidate the American farmer and cast a cloud on his integrity by such a charge. Mr. Caplin should be made to prove his sweeping indictment or apologize to the American farmer." It appeared that Mr. Caplin also experienced some intimidation.

For some reason or other a colossal indifference to the city taxpayer's stake in agricultural policy pervades the thinking of farm organizations and their leadership. The latter seem convinced that the choice of farm programs will forever be left solely to farmers even though they do not pick up the tab. To some extent Congress shares this myopia when it presents its own program to farmers for their approval or disapproval. It assumes that the public stands ready with a checkbook; that farmers need only agree among themselves about how they will qualify for "benefit payments." This obliviousness to the general interest has led to delays in arriving at basic decisions and to substantial increases in the costs of farm programs.

TOO MUCH OF A GOOD THING

In 1961 the tiny state of Delaware experienced an overproduction of commercial beauty culture. It was the flowering of a problem that had grown more acute year by year. Delicious looking females had seemingly become so common throughout the state, and those who groomed them had become so efficient, that alarm gripped the cosmetic salons. Departing from a traditional attachment to free enterprise, the beauticians, manicurists, and masseuses of the First State connived to persuade the state legislature to apply government controls to the practice of their arts.

They were judicious in their approach. With the sureness of feminine intuition these beauty practitioners sensed that perhaps no male would be so crass as to endorse government restrictions upon chic and charm. To forward their cause they prevailed upon State Senator Margaret R. Manning to introduce bill SB 251 to create a State Board of Cosmetology which would regulate and license the "Arranging, dressing, curling, waiving . . . on the hair . . . the use of cosmetic preparations . . . massaging, cleansing . . . stimulating, manipulating, exercising, beautifying or similar work on the scalp, face, neck, arms, hands, bust, or upper part of the body, or manicuring the nails of any person."[13] So thorough was this assault upon the freedom of women to be lovely without benefit of state supervision that the gentlemen of the senate, with proper regard for their own self-interest, voted to postpone decision to the following year. If legislators of succeeding sessions are as chivalrous the issue may not be resolved. The dalliance of Congress over farm policy has afforded precedent for legislative indecision, although never with such sensitive purpose.

SOMETHING FOR NOTHING

While the public may not be greatly aroused by the fate of cosmeticians, it has been shaken by the realization that costs of crop programs, instead of diminishing, are on the increase. Instead of solving old problems, commodity programs have created new ones. Although there are only half as many farmers today as there were in the thirties when government aid was first broadly extended, farm appropriations have multiplied many times. As farmers have become fewer, more efficient, and wealthier they have demanded more public aid and gotten it. To the urban mind this does not seem reasonable. On every side the city taxpayer observes an urgent need for local public services which he cannot afford. Yet he sees the federal government spend billions to buy farm produce which it then turns over to those who rent storage facilities.

The state of Pennsylvania knows what industrial depression is since its urban unemployment rate has been among the highest in the nation for several years. As a recent editorial in the Harrisburg *Patriot*[14] made clear, some people in the state capitol take a dim view of rewarding successful farmers with government checks while local industry falters: "If the 1961–62 farm outlays weren't necessary, the First National City Bank of New York reported after a farm subsidy study, no one would pay income taxes at a rate exceeding 20 percent. The bank did some fancy arithmetic and came up with a per capita figure of $1,700 which Uncle Sam lays out every year for every farmer in the United States. But let no one be under any illusion that the little farmer, the so-called family farmer, is making out under this Federal program. He's not getting anywhere near $1,700. The per capita average comes out this high only because the big corporation farms clean up so much. . . . Under our fantastic agriculture subsidy system, we continue to build up ever-larger surpluses with ever-fewer farmers. The poor get poorer and the rich get richer, as Uncle Sam hands out the cash . . ."

Senator Edward V. Long of Missouri told his colleagues in May of 1962 that he thought the submission of urban citizens to taxation for farm subsidies would not last much longer. Said Senator Long, "I can detect among Members of Congress representing large metropolitan areas a feeling that they cannot much longer support agricultural bills which continue to pile up costly surpluses, and undue burdens on the taxpayers."[15] This urban sentiment seems also to have rung a bell in the Department of Agriculture. One month later Secretary Freeman told newspaper correspondents who had spoken of outcries against the mounting costs of farm programs: "I don't know where the break point comes.

But I do know the temper of Congress and the temper of the country. We gave a choice for farmers in our bill. They could control production in return for support, or go it alone. If Congress erupts one day, the farmers won't have that choice."[16] The bill Mr. Freeman referred to was that new proposal of his department to drop price supports unless farmers accepted mandatory acreage reductions of crops which are in surplus.

POLITICAL CORN

Among the costliest of all farm programs is the one which supports the prices of livestock feed grains: corn, sorghums, barley, and oats. Since livestock and their products represent more than half the value of all agricultural marketings, it is easy to comprehend the far-reaching influence of the feed grain program — and the fact that Congress faces it with the greatest reluctance and the greatest variety of compromise.

A prevailing opinion among corn belt farmers is that any reduction in feed grain acreages should be voluntary but price supports should be mandatory. Lower Middle Class farmers rightly claim that fixed allotments would prevent them from getting bigger as they would have to do if they were to catch up with the technological revolution. With equal correctness big farmers complain that "controls" would cheat them out of advantages they have gained by being efficient under the free enterprise system. As one Indiana grower told a visitor, "What would appeal to us most would be strong price supports with no controls." Then he added with a grin, "But, of course, we can't have everything." Recognition by the corn-hog farmer that he cannot have everything does not prevent him from trying. He would like corn prices pegged at levels where he can make a profit by feeding grain to the government if he does not feed it to hogs. With equal insistence he objects to what Charles B. Shuman, president of the Farm Bureau, refers to as giving government the "power to club the farmer's brains out."[17]

The Kennedy administration's Food and Agriculture Act of

1962 departed from thirty years of precedent when it recommended that all feed grain farmers either accept strict acreage controls or become ineligible for price supports. When this measure came into the House most corn belt representatives jumped on it with both feet, and they were no small factor in its defeat by a vote of 215 to 205. Having failed in its first attempt to clip this part of the farm budget, the administration was obliged to change its approach. It fell back to what was essentially the Eisenhower-Benson position which the corn belt had torpedoed when the Republicans were in office. Ezra Taft Benson of Utah guided policy for the Department of Agriculture in those crucial years when the costs of farm price supports made their great leap forward. Those were the days when it became apparent to all that the technological revolution had given farmers a capacity to out-produce the Treasury as long as the government was committed to buy at profitable prices whatever was not consumed.

The key to the Benson program was the level at which the government might have been obliged to support prices. If support prices were high they would stimulate unnecessary production by specialists. If they just covered the costs of production by the most efficient, they might put the Lower Middle Class growers in jeopardy. Benson wanted price levels close to costs of production by the most efficient farmers to dissuade big producers from overloading the government storage bins at the taxpayer's expense. Throughout the eight years Secretary Benson was in office he never received authority from Congress to put government supports down to where he thought they belonged. The average support price of corn during his tenure ranged from a high of $1.62 in 1954 to a low of $1.06 in 1960.

Ezra Taft Benson is generally regarded as having been a failure in office, but it was a failure imposed by Congress, which hog-tied him from the start because of pressures back home. It would be easy to anticipate that under such a program the Lower Middle Class corn-livestock farmer would be at a disadvantage in competition with others who operate on a larger scale with more modern equipment; so they objected. It is also easy to see that with floor prices raised to a level which would keep the Lower Middle Class afloat, the specialists in the upper brackets could have a field day growing surpluses for the public treasury. Since that was a rather tempting prospect they, too, objected. Government stocks of corn rose from 736 million bushels in 1954 to 1,675 million bushels in 1960.[18] In 1961 specialized cash-corn growers in the corn belt averaged 86 bushels per acre. Specialized corn-livestock farmers, who raised corn for their own use, had average yields of 61 to 84 bushels per acre. A 1962 study by the Ohio Agricultural Experiment Station[19] indicates that the costs of corn production in the corn belt of west central Ohio in 1958 were $62.82 per acre for small farms of 50 to 141 acres while they were $55.33 per acre on farms of 364 to 996 acres. These figures indicate that some specialists able to produce 84 bushels per acre can now raise corn for 66 cents a bushel. It is well known that the best technicians are getting average yields of over 100 bushels per acre and so are producing for even less.

When the Eisenhower-Benson plan became the fall-back position of the Kennedy-Freeman administration during the final battles of the 87th Congress, it again encountered opposition from the corn belt. However, the measure squeaked through to the surprise of many. It is scheduled to become operative in 1964 unless the 88th Congress modifies or replaces it. As it read in the autumn of 1962 the Freeman version of the old Benson plan would pay farmers to retire land voluntarily. It would also set the lowest limit for corn support prices at 50 per cent of parity.* Translated into

---

* Parity was a term widely used in the nineteen twenties and thirties to indicate the price at which a farmer would have to sell a given quantity of farm goods to buy the manufactured articles he could have bought had he made both transactions at the parity date. Parity, of course, was a casualty of the technological revolution in agriculture because that revolution raised efficiency on farms at a far faster rate than efficiency in industry improved. It has made no sense to claim parity for farmers in recent years because their unit costs of production have generally declined while industry, on the other hand, has experienced a general increase in unit costs of production. The term parity is still used, however, as a measuring stick and as a political gimmick.

cash this would mean a floor of about 80 cents a bushel instead of the $1.20 which has prevailed since 1961. Since the cost of production by the most efficient cash grain growers is around 60 to 70 cents, there is still room for profit, but the margin is so greatly reduced that overplanting would not be likely. Since the idea of parity became popular in the 1930's feed grain production per man-hour has increased more than eight times. This phenomenal increase in agricultural efficiency makes the parity concept obsolete.

The Freeman version of the Benson bill gives the Secretary power to choke off surpluses which Benson never enjoyed. The language of the legislation makes it mandatory that the lowest permissible support prices prevail if the Secretary of Agriculture believes that anything higher would result in additions to government stocks already in storage. If farmers do not want to accept strict allotments without federal subsidies, then to the urban tax payer this arrangement may be an acceptable alternative.

Republican Karl E. Mundt of South Dakota was prominent among those in the Senate who denounced the new bill as too severe. On September 21, several days before it was enacted into law, he informed his colleagues: "It seems to me that this legislation, as it comes to us from conference, heralds the collapse of the whole price support concept in agriculture, and provides, in lieu of a fairly satisfactory and rewarding system of price supports, a system of fluctuating price supports, worse by far in their impact on farmers than anything that was ever presented to us by Secretary Benson or the Department of Agriculture. As is well known, Secretary Benson himself was an advocate of flexible price supports. This proposal goes further than the Benson flexible price philosophy, because it not only provides a further flexing of prices downward, but it is tied to an anchor instead of to a star."[21] Senator Mundt stated what the urban taxpayer had long suspected: that agricultural price supports had been hitched to a star.

In the House, Iowa's Representative Charles B. Hoeven, the minority leader of the House Committee on Agriculture, expressed his disapproval of the new bill when it came up for debate.

". . . in a very clever move," said Mr. Hoeven, "the Senate has sought to amend the Agricultural Act of 1958 whereby the Secretary of Agriculture will be given complete discretion and authority to fix the price support on corn from zero to 90 percent, of parity provided that none such feed grains help build up the Commodity Credit Corporation's stocks on corn. This provision is dangerous because it will practically mean removing all price supports on corn. . . . Everyone knows whenever you have cheap feed grains, you are going to have cheap livestock, so another problem will be created."[22] The taxpaying consumer who had to pay for raising the price of corn may not have realized that by so doing he was also boosting the cost of meat above what it would have been otherwise.

The year 1964 seemed a long way off in the autumn of 1962. No political realist expected that a bill passed then would go unchallenged by the new Congress in 1963. J. H. Carmical of the *New York Times* forecast a battle that would be of interest to the taxpayer at large. Said he, "Farmers generally do not want drastic Government controls over production and they do not want support prices as low as 80 cents a bushel on corn and less than $1 on wheat. That is why new farm legislation next year is almost a certainty."[23]

The November elections of 1962 indicated that voters were losing their sympathy for farm interests. *Wallaces Farmer,* a voice to reckon with in the corn belt, had seen this coming as early as January, 1962, when it editorialized in criticism of those farmers who favored high spending programs without controls. "New programs will have more teeth, more compulsory features. We've had farm program fights practically every year. But they were mostly family spats — differences of opinion among farmers themselves. Now a third party, the city consumer, armed with new voting power, is watching these goings on in Washington with increasing interest and suspicion. With this new 'partner' aboard, farm legislation must be drawn more carefully. To avoid a violent consumer revolt at the polls, political leaders know that future farm programs must be less costly and more effective."[24] In October, *Wallaces Farmer* again commented: "The narrowness of the 202–197 margin by which it [the farm bill for 1964] was passed by the House is evidence of the struggle. It was a battle between USDA and the Farm Bureau. No sooner had each member of Congress received a letter from the AFBF President Shuman urging defeat of the bill, than a letter of opposite urging arrived from Secretary Freeman."[25] It was pretty certain that Freeman and Shuman would be at it again. The dust hardly had settled after the November elections when the protagonists met in the Secretary's office. The Secretary's assistants had let it be known to the press that they felt the new Congress would help them institute controls and cut spending. Farm Bureau Federation officials disagreed. The taxpayer would watch in 1965 to see who was right, for he had a major interest in the outcome.

IN RETROSPECT

There were several ironical aspects to the feed grains subsidy program as it was administered in recent years. In the first place the government was committed to make storage loans on corn at prices above open market quotations yet producers were not obliged to restrict production. Those who volunteered to cut down their plantings received additional "compensatory payments." Because its support prices were liberal, the government had to pay generously for voluntary acreage reduction. The Treasury was in the position of bidding against itself. Such approaches were naturally expensive and ineffective. They were essentially political rather than businesslike arrangements. The abundant harvests that poured in annually were no miracle; they were a predictable response to congressional largess. While the gullible taxpayer held an umbrella over prices he got splashed by those who overproduced precisely because he held the umbrella.

This particular point was well outlined for Michigan Congressman Charles E. Chamberlain by a home state grain merchant. "There is only one reason why we are troubled with surplus," wrote the constituent, "and that is because of unrealistic support prices. You guarantee a producer a good profit and he'll sure set new records every year. With today's low production costs, $2 wheat and $1.20 corn prices are too high and everybody who is aware of the facts knows it. . . . Regardless of what you hear from the people who claim to speak for the farmer, production costs per bushel or hundredweight are at all time lows and the desire to hold prices per unit at or above historical levels is unrealistic. . . . The only farm program that can succeed and preserve the free enterprise system which we know in our hearts provides the best way of life for the most people, is a program of low supports or crop insurance to prevent disaster and let the efficient farmers produce those crops for which there is a market and in volume that will provide a fair profit."[26]

Many others were also cognizant of the irrationality of the existing feed grains program. The *Nashville Tennessean* stated in June, 1962 when the administration's first farm bill was about to come up for the House vote which killed it: "The Kennedy farm bill, which at last will give American farmers the opportunity to put livestock feed-grain production on a realistic basis, comes up for House floor action soon, probably this week. The bill, already approved by the Senate, sets strict production controls that go into effect only if the farmers involved approve them in referendum by a two-thirds majority. If they do not approve the controls, price supports will drop sharply and may be eliminated. This is sensible legislation which recognizes two important facts from which Congress has been hiding too long — that purely voluntary controls will not work, and that the Government cannot go on piling up surpluses by the billions of dollars."[27]

The *Wall Street Journal* is not preferred bedtime reading in the corn belt; its point of view is more likely to produce nightmares than sweet dreams. However, this is the way that ticker tape tip sheet looked at agriculture in the late summer of 1962. "The day is approaching, slowly or not," wrote feature columnist Paul Duke, "when Congress will fundamentally alter Federal farm laws. . . . days of drift seem numbered. For all its dallying, Congress seems inevitably headed toward accepting the challenges laid down by two successive Secretaries of Agriculture. These challenges of Ezra Taft Benson, Republican, and Orville L. Freeman, Democrat, agreed on just one crucial point: The Government cannot go on forever giving farmers both artificially high prices and freedom to produce. Secretary Benson's proposals essentially aimed at denying them the former. Secretary Freeman's planning basically aims at denying them the latter. Congress, unwilling to accept either harsh prescription, has year after year voted a mishmash — headed neither toward a consistent low-price, free-market agriculture nor inward a tightly regimented high-price farm economy. Yet the course of historic events now makes it practically certain the lawmakers will at least turn down either one road or the other."[28]

In view of a hardening urban attitude toward increasingly heavy outlays for agriculture, farmers in the numerous but depressed Lower Middle Class will soon have to make up their minds as to whether they want tight controls that will help them keep their present 23 per cent of the market without public aid or whether they want to take their chances in open competition. A fateful decision on this issue cannot be deferred indefinitely. A reluctance to face the choice has characterized the past decade and is reflected in the saying going the rounds among farmers who dislike either alternative — "Benson made a Democrat out of me and now Freeman is turning me back into a Republican."

The basic reason drastic measures must be taken, particularly by the Lower Middle Class, is that if this group of 1.3 million farmers were out of agriculture entirely the remaining farmers in the First and Upper Middle Classes could take care of themselves. The fundamental weakness of the Lower Middle Class, and one that can hardly be remedied at this late stage of technological development, is that it is undercapitalized in an age when farm efficiency calls for a high level of capitalization. Labor income is low. The returns from capital investment are more satisfactory. The contrast between these two kinds of returns is illustrated in Table 10, which is constructed from data in the Department of Agriculture's 1962 study of farm costs and returns on 39 different types of farms. (See also Table 13.)

In view of the undercapitalized condition of the Lower Middle Class, it would seem that the time is coming when the best the average operator in this distressed group can hope for will be underemployment or part-time employment in farming. By modern standards he does not have a physical plant that is large enough or up-to-date enough to fully and efficiently employ himself. Instead of a public supported agricultural relief program, he needs what the undercapitalized, underemployed or part-time employed urban citizen needs — expanded work opportunities on the payroll of others who have capital to create jobs. Then this farmer could commute to work and keep his rural home as many in his class already do. The mathematics of disadvantage as far as the Lower Middle Class is concerned is not likely to improve, and figures show that this group is already far behind. On an average the 1.3 million farmers in the Lower Middle Class have only one-fifth as much capacity to produce as the average farmers among the 0.8 million in the upper brackets — thus their physical base for making a decent living is only one-fifth as good. (Table 13.)

The general public should hardly be expected to make up for this deficiency in capital assets through subsidies. If it were, then every unemployed urban citizen might conclude that it is also a public responsibility to set him up in business if he cannot find a job. One of the strangest aspects of public policy at the present time is the highly articulate concern about the low incomes of 1.3 million undercapitalized entrepreneurs in agriculture's Lower Middle Class while other more serious social and economic calamities have befallen the more numerous families of the urban unemployed who have less income and less equity in property. Certainly the democratic way of life is more threatened by growing urban slums than it is by the decline of the undercapitalized family farm, but as yet there is not even a Department of Urban Affairs in the federal government.

BUILD-UP

The clamor for federal participation in farm market affairs began in the twenties when two western Republicans, Senator Charles McNary and Representative Gilbert N. Haugen, first raised the issue in a specific bill. Responding to pressure from farm organizations which wanted to get a reluctant government into farming, the two legislators proposed to Congress that it establish a corporation and supply it with federal funds to buy enough of each major export crop to raise prices in the United States above world market levels. President Calvin Coolidge, a thrifty New Englander, did not think much of the idea and vetoed it in 1928. Said "Silent Cal," a man as sparing of words as of the nation's purse: "Government price-fixing, once started, has alike no justice and no end."[29] On this subject the Republican President echoed the stand of Democrats who had already said in 1928: "The solution to this problem should avoid Government subsidies, to which the Democratic Party has always been opposed."[29]

The farm lobbies' bright new idea that government should get into agriculture did not stay vetoed long. In 1929, under California's Herbert Hoover, farm leaders got their way and the government began to tap the Treasury in an effort to boost prices. From that time on, regardless of which political party has been in power, the taxpayer has become increasingly committed to paying bigger farm subsidies. Plowmen in business suits have learned that no seed yields a better harvest than that planted in the fertile minds of Congress. In 1962 when Secretary Freeman boasted that the Democratic Party's farm program of 1961 had raised farmers' income a billion dollars over that of the Republican program of 1960 he neglected to mention that over three-quarters of this rise was in the form of government aid.[30] Farmers got $791 million more in direct government payments under Mr. Freeman in 1961 than they had received the year before under Mr. Benson.[31] The technological revolution in the field and in the barn had never done so much for the farmer in one year as this technological revolution in political haymaking.

From the Hoover administration's Agriculture Marketing Act of 1929 to the Benson plan under Eisenhower and on down to the Kennedy-Freeman Act of 1961 the pace quickened and became vastly more expensive. All along the line farm organizations lobbied for greater government spending and less government interference with their "free enterprise system." They did so well that in 1961 when total net farm income reached $12.9 billion the taxpayers' not-so-free-enterprise system contributed $5.9 billion to Department of Agriculture programs to support that income.[32] Apparently it was a good year, for during the twelve months of 1961 farmers' net equities in property increased by $3.4 billion[33] — an average of almost $1,000 for each "census farmer." Nevertheless, in agriculture nothing seems to fail like success. Farm lobbyists cried that the government had tortured them on the socialist rack, so Congress eased the screws a little and authorized the Department of Agriculture to spend an estimated $7.2 billion in 1962.[34]

Complaints about "federal dictatorship" have been standard stage script for farm lobbies throughout the years, for it seems that to bite the hand that feeds almost invariably results in bigger handouts. According to the *Congressional Record*,[35] two farm organizations were among the top ten of Washington's big spending lobbies in 1961. The combined outlays of the American Farm Bureau Federation and the National Farmers Union amounted to more than the expenditures of the wealthy American Medical Association, which led all the rest in promoting self-interest. Also among the first ten were two labor organizations, two investment groups, one veterans' organization, one trucking association, and a housing conference.

THE AVALANCHE

Although the taxpayer has been buying crop surpluses to boost the market prices of agricultural commodities for more than three decades, the net cost to the government did not get out of hand until the late 1950's. Despite all the furor in the early thirties over the New Deal's "plowed-under cotton" and the "slaughter of little pigs" the total costs of these efforts seem infinitesimal by today's standards. For the twenty years 1932–51 the net losses to the taxpayer for subsidies to stabilize farm prices was only $6.8 billion, or $343 million a year.[36] A big jump came when the total loss or "realized cost" of commodity programs reached $22.1 billion for the decade 1952–61 — an average of $2.2 billion a year. Senator Richard B. Russell of Georgia summarized the story of public deficit spending on farm surpluses in recent years in a concise table which he placed in the *Congressional Record* on August 25, 1962. It showed that the "realized cost," or loss, for the decade 1952–61 was over $22 billion and that the cost for 1961 alone reached $5.2 billion as compared with the 1952 "realized cost" of $280 million. (See Table 14.) Clearly the price support program had gone into orbit and it was time to fire an anti-missile missile.

DECISION

Perhaps the problem of finding a program on which agriculturists can agree has gone beyond rational solution because farmers are at odds with one another in their objectives. Some want to expand, others would settle for the *status quo*. Farmers in deficit areas resent being restricted while surplus crops pour into their states from other areas. Poultry raisers who buy feeds are against any kind of controls which would reduce their supplies or raise their costs. Corn growers want freedom to produce yet they want the market price of their products supported.

No Secretary of Agriculture with a slide rule and the wisdom of Solomon could satisfy these competing demands. The only new development in the farm picture which may force a compromise decision is the conscious entry of the man from whose wallet the benefit payments come. Now Congress must weigh not only the strength of contending farm opinions, it must also reckon with the man who signs the checks. As approaches to the farm problem in the past have been political, so they are most likely to be in the future. As city dwellers grow more articulate and reapportionment gives them a stronger voice in formulating those particular farm policies that involve public money, they will have a greater influence on legislative decisions.

There is no solution which will not hurt some farmers and benefit others. Even to abandon all farm programs would be a boon to some agriculturists and a catastrophe to others. Like everyone else in a dynamic society, farmers are changing as the economy changes around them. Some who were sitting pretty two decades ago now find themselves in the Lower Middle Class. Others who never dreamed they would own a steer are in First Class, feeding several thousand. A law passed to save someone in trouble may turn out to offer an incentive to a fast operator to pull his money out of merchant shipping and put it into cotton. Again, as Calvin Coolidge said: "Government price-fixing, once started, has alike no justice and no end." The immediate burden of decision, however, falls on the 1.3 million farmers in the Lower Middle Class. Will they accept the admittedly hard consolation prize of 23 per cent of the market divided among them or do they want to face their competition on a free enterprise basis? There is no point in trying to keep alive the old shopworn concept of the family farm when the real character of the family farm has drastically changed from a labor institution to a business capital institution and the number of farm families is about half of what it was a quarter of a century ago.

Now that farm subsidies run around $5.0 billion a year instead of about $0.3 billion as they did in 1952, the taxpayer is entitled to believe that the point of diminishing returns has been reached. For the moment, at least, he may feel he has put enough public money into agriculture. The fact that farm lobbies have grown bigger and bolder and surpluses have become mammoth indicates that a stage of gigantism has been reached. Biologically, if not economically, gigantism indicates the climax of an evolutionary process. The end of a process, however, does not mean an end to all evolution. To the contrary, as far as American agriculture is concerned, perhaps the end of big government spending will mark the beginning of new and more intensive efforts by farmers to manage their businesses and seek their personal fortunes in more sophisticated ways.

As for the urbanite, there are other matters of public concern which are far more worthy of a $5 billion program than crop surpluses. The sorry condition of the metropolitan environment and the dilapidated state of public services in the city indicate that these problems require more than casual attention. If the welfare of the American family is of real significance to the nation's policy makers, let them look forward to the city where most of those families live, instead of backward to the country which most of them have abandoned.

Source References

CHAPTER 1 The Technological Revolution

1 *Evening Bulletin,* Philadelphia, May 10, 1961

2 *Historical Statistics of the United States — Colonial Times to 1957,*
   U. S. Department of Commerce, 1960, p. 278

3 *Yearbook of Agriculture, 1960, U. S. Department of Agriculture,*
   p. 169

4 *Historical Statistics of the United States — Colonial Times to 1957,*
   U. S. Department of Commerce, 1960, p. 285

   Statistical Abstract of the United States, 1962, Bureau of the Census, p. 607

5 *Food and Agriculture: A Program for the 1960's,* U. S. Department of Agriculture, March, 1962, p. 8

6 *Food and Agriculture: A Program for the 1960's,* U. S. Department of Agriculture, March, 1962, p. 50

7 *Philadelphia Inquirer,* June 24, 1959

8 *New York Times,* April 21, 1962

9 *New York Times,* April 29, 1962 and May 11, 1962

10 *Statistical Abstract of the United States, 1961,* pp. 613 and 628

11 *Statistical Abstract of the United States, 1962,* p. 629

12 *The Balance Sheet of Agriculture, 1961,* U. S. Department of Agriculture, p. 2

13 *Agricultural Policy Issues; Selected Readings,* Farm Foundation, 1956, p. 60

14 *Wallaces Farmer,* January 20, 1962, p. 12

15 *New York Times,* December 19, 1961

16 *Background on Our Nation's Agriculture,* Leaflet No. 491, U. S. Department of Agriculture, 1961

17 *Agricultural Statistics, 1960,* U. S. Department of Agriculture, p. 581

18 *Food Is a Bargain,* Marketing Bulletin No. 18, U. S. Department of Agriculture, May, 1961

19 *Background on Our Nation's Agriculture,* Leaflet No. 491, U. S. Department of Agriculture, 1961

21 *Congressional Record,* February 21, 1962, p. 2487

22 *New York Times,* April 25, 1960

23 *Ohio Farm and Home Research,* Wooster, Ohio, Vol. 45, No. 6, November–December, 1960

24 *Progressive Farmer,* December, 1961, p. 11

25 *New York Times,* January 19, 1958

27 *New York Times,* November 12, 1957

28 *Evening Bulletin,* Philadelphia, January 5, 1962

29 *United States Census of Agriculture, 1959,* Vol. II, Chapter 7, pp. 854–55

30 *Farm and Ranch,* January, 1962

33 *New York Times,* April 5, 1962

34 *Agricultural Statistics, 1961,* U. S. Department of Agriculture, p. 419

35 *Arkansas Gazette,* Little Rock, December 10, 1961

36 *Farm Journal*

37 *Journal Every Evening,* Wilmington, Delaware, November 26, 1957

38 *Time*

39 *Concentration and Ownership in Food Marketing Industries,* Stephen J. Hiemstra, Economic Research Service, U. S. Department of Agriculture, 1962, Table 10

40 *New York Herald Tribune,* December 18, 1961

41 *New York Times,* March 18, 1962

42 *Congressional Record,* June 14, 1962, p. A4433

43 *Statistical Abstract of the United States, 1962,* p. 639

44 *Balance Sheet of Agriculture, 1962,* U. S. Department of Agriculture, p. 5

45 *Progressive Farmer,* December, 1961, p. 62

46 *Wallaces Farmer,* February 3, 1962

47 *New York Times,* August 25, 1962

48 *United States Census of Agriculture, 1959, Vol. II, Chapter 6, Table 26*

49 *United States Census of Agriculture, 1959,* Vol. II, Chapter 11, Table 5

CHAPTER 2 Who Is the American Farmer?

1 *Food and Agriculture: A Program for the 1960's,* U. S. Department of Agriculture, 1962, p. 50

2 *Agricultural Statistics, 1961,* U. S. Department of Agriculture, 1962, p. 435

3 *Wallaces Farmer,* February 3, 1962, p. 15

5 *Resource Requirements on Farms for Specified Operator Incomes,* Harold E. Barnhill, U. S. Department of Agriculture, Economic Research Service, F.E.D., February, 1962, p. 6

6 *New York Times,* June 15, 1962

7 *United States Census of Agriculture, 1959,* Vol. II, Chap. 11, Table 5

8 *Statistical Abstract of the United States, 1961,* p. 613

9 *Statistical Abstract of the United States, 1961*, p. 629

10 *Congressional Record*, September 21, 1962, p. A7011

11 *Potato Production Costs, Central Aroostook, 1958 and 1959*, Winston E. Pullen and Dean F. Tuthill, Maine Agricultural Experimental Station, Orono, April 5, 1961, p. 4

12 *Wilmington Morning News*, April 3, 1962

13 *Farm Journal*, April, 1962, p. 49

14 *New York Times*, March 24, 1958

15 *Farm Journal*, October, 1962, p. 10

16 *New York Times*, September 6, 1962

17 *U. S. News & World Report*, November 5, 1962, p. 10

18 *New York Times*, September 2, 1962

19 *Evening Bulletin*, Philadelphia, October 1, 1962

20 *Providence Journal*, September 18, 1962

21 *New York Times*, September 11, 1962 and September 13, 1962

22 *New York Times*, September 7, 1962

23 *Farm and Ranch*, October, 1962

24 *New York Times* (Magazine Sec.), September 16, 1962

25 *Congressional Record*, September 14, 1962, p. A6847

26 *Wallaces Farmer*, November 17, 1962, p. 44

27 *New York Times* (Magazine Sec.), December 2, 1962

CHAPTER 3   The Farm in the
American Mind

1 *New York Times*, February 18, 1960

2 *Letters From an American Farmer*, J. Hector St. John Crèvecoeur, Dolphin Books, Doubleday & Company, Garden City, N. Y. (no date), p. 7

3 *Farming and Democracy,* A. Whitney Griswold, Yale University Press, New Haven, 1952, p. 4

4 *Jefferson and Agriculture,* Everett E. Edwards, U. S. Department of Agriculture, Agricultural History Series No. 7, 1943, p. 23

5 *Time,* June 29, 1962, p. 10

7 *Changes in Farms and Farming,* H. L. Stewart, An Address Before the 39th Annual Agricultural Outlook Conference, Washington, D. C., November 16, 1961, p. 10 of release

8 *Congressional Record,* May 7, 1962, p. A3334

9 *Evening Journal,* Wilmington, Delaware, April 13, 1962

10 *New York Times,* Sunday, March 25, 1962

11 *United States Census of Agriculture, 1959,* Vol. II, Chapter 11, Table 5

12 *New York Times,* July 22, 1962

CHAPTER 4 Land and the Demand for Space

1 *Evening Journal,* Wilmington, Delaware, July 5, 1962

2 *Des Moines Sunday Register,* November 5, 1961

3 *Statistical Abstract of the United States, 1961,* p. 613, also p. 5

4 *Agricultural Statistics, 1961,* U. S. Department of Agriculture, p. 436

5 *Evening Journal,* Wilmington, Delaware, July 26, 1962

6 *Statistical Abstract of the United States, 1961,* p. 619

7 *Cotton Farms San Joaquin Valley California Organization, Costs and Returns 1947–1959,* Agricultural Economic Report No. 3, U. S. Department of Agriculture, December, 1961, p. 21

8 *An Adaptive Program for Agriculture: A Statement on National Policy by the Research and Policy Committee for Economic Development,* New York, July, 1962

9   *Congressional Record*, June 18, 1962, pp. 10125–27

10   *Congressional Record*, August 8, 1962, p. 14880

11   *Statistical Abstract of the United States, 1961*, p. 628

12   *Statistical Abstract of the United States, 1961*, p. 614

13   *Congressional Record*, March 1, 1962, p. 2918

14   *Evening Journal*, Wilmington, Delaware, May 14, 1961

15   *Congressional Record*, August 9, 1962, p. 15040

16   *Project Twenty-Twelve*, U. S. Department of the Interior, pp. 38–
     40

17   *Statistical Abstract of the United States, 1961*, pp. 189–90

18   *New York Times*, July 16, 1961

19   *Statistical Abstract of the United States, 1962*, p. 201

20   *Statistical Abstract of the United States, 1961*, p. 194

21   *Morning News*, Wilmington, Delaware, August 10, 1962

22   *Congressional Record*, May 17, 1962, pp. A3728–30

23   *New York Times*, October 3, 1962

CHAPTER 5   Debate and Decision

1   *Statistical Abstract of the United States, 1962*, p. 608

2   *Congressional Record*, July 17, 1962, pp. 12897–98

3   *New York Times*, August 23, 1962

4   *Congressional Record*, February 15, 1962, p. 2135

5   *Congressional Record*, May 24, 1962, p. 8559

7   *New York Times*, September 23, 1962

8   *Statistical Abstract of the United States, 1962*, pp. 5 and 608

9   *New York Times*, October 15, 1962

10   *New York Times*, May 12, 1958

11 *Congressional Record,* April 2, 1962, p. A2512, and August 31, 1962, p. 17223

12 *Congressional Record,* May 21, 1962, p. 8170

13 *Evening Journal,* Wilmington, Delaware, December 26, 1961

14 *Patriot,* Harrisburg, Pa., from *Congressional Record,* June 6, 1962, p. A4138

15 *Congressional Record,* May 23, 1962, p. 8315

16 *New York Times,* June 24, 1962

17 *Arkansas Gazette,* February 25, 1962

18 *Grain and Feed Statistics Through 1961,* Statistical Bulletin No. 159, U. S. Department of Agriculture, June, 1962, p. 47

19 *Ohio Agricultural Experiment Station Research Bulletin 909,* R. H. Blosser, June, 1962, p. 13

21 *Congressional Record,* September 21, 1962, p. 19213

22 *Congressional Record,* August 30, 1962, p. 17186

23 *New York Times,* November 4, 1962

24 *Wallaces Farmer,* January 6, 1962, p. 12

25 *Wallaces Farmer,* October 6, 1962

26 *Congressional Record,* February 8, 1962, pp. A993–94

27 *Congressional Record,* June 14, 1962, p. A4453

28 *Congressional Record,* August 8, 1962, p. 14908

29 *Congressional Record,* February 21, 1962, p. A1306

30 *Congressional Record,* March 28, 1962, p. A2421

31 *Statistical Abstract of the United States, 1962,* p. 630

32 *Statistical Abstract of the United States, 1962,* pp. 630 and 381

33 *Statistical Abstract of the United States, 1962,* p. 629

34 *Statistical Abstract of the United States, 1962,* p. 381

35 *Congressional Record,* September 19, 1962, p. A6930

36 *Can We Solve the Farm Problem?* Murray R. Benedict, The Twentieth Century Fund, New York, 1955, pp. 474–75

Appendices

TABLE I   Value of Production, by Class[a] of Farm, 1959

Class of Farm	Number	Per Cent of Total	Value Class	Value of Net Production in Billions	Per Cent of Total Value of All Farm Sales
Elite	1,200	1–	$500,000+	$ 1.4	4.6
Jr. Elite	21,000	1–	100,000–500,000	3.8	12.4
Blue Ribbon	80,000	2+	40,000–100,000	4.4	14.5
Remainder of First Class	210,402	6	20,000–40,000	5.6	18.4
Upper Middle	483,004	13	10,000–20,000	6.7	21.9
Lower Middle	1,271,558	34	2,500–10,000	7.0	22.8
Third	1,640,910	44	2,500–	1.6	5.3
TOTAL, ALL FARMS	3,708,000	100		$30.6	99.9

SOURCES: *Census of Agriculture, 1959*, Vol. II, Chapter 11, Table 5 and p. 1200; and Series AC–59–1, p. 3.
Note: Discrepancies in addition are due to rounding.
[a] Class names used in this table are comparable with census classes as follows:

Table 1	Census
Elite, Jr. Elite, Blue Ribbon	Class I Commercial
Remainder of First Class	Class II Commercial
Upper Middle Class	Class III Commercial
Lower Middle Class	Classes IV & V Commercial
Third Class	Class VI Commercial, Part-time, Part-retirement

TABLE 2   Changes in Farm Class[a] and Percentages
of Sales, 1950 to 1959

	Number in Thousands		Percentage Distribution	
Farm Class	*1950*	*1959*	*1950*	*1959*
Combined First and Upper Middle }	484	794	9.0	21.5
Lower Middle	1,603	1,270	29.8	34.3
Third	3,291	1,637	61.2	44.2
	Dollar Sales in Millions		Per Cent of Market	
Farm Class	*1950*	*1959*	*1950*	*1959*
First and Upper Middle	$11,303	$21,860	50.7	71.7
Lower Middle	8,268	6,989	37.1	23.0
Third	2,340	1,775	12.2	5.3

[a] See Table 1 for description of classes.
Source: Census of Agriculture, 1959, Vol. II, Chapter 11, p. 1206.

TABLE 3 Characteristics of Farms, by Class[a] and Type,[b] 1959

Type[b] of Farm	Geographic Center of Production[c]			Class[a] of Farms		
	1st	2nd	3rd	First	Upper Middle	Lower Middle
Cash grain	W.N.C.	E.N.C.				
Number of farms				47,000	101,000	217,000
Per cent of all sales				39%	32%	28%
Tobacco	S.A.	E.S.C.				
Number of farms				2,000	12,000	120,000
Per cent of all sales				9%	17%	65%
Cotton	E.S.C.	W.S.C.	S.A.			
Number of farms				29,000	25,000	105,000
Per cent of all sales				63%	13%	20%
Other field crops[d]	S.A.	W.S.C.	Mt.			
Number of farms				9,000	9,000	15,000
Per cent of all sales				74%	15%	10%
Vegetable	Pac.	S.A.	E.N.C & M.A.			
Number of farms				5,000	3,500	9,000
Per cent of all sales				84%	8%	7%

TABLE 3 (continued)

Type[b] of Farm	Geographic Center of Production[c]			Class[a] of Farms		
	1st	2nd	3rd	First	Upper Middle	Lower Middle
Fruit & nut	Pac.	S.A.				
Number of farms				16,000	13,000	28,000
Per cent of all sales				73%	14%	13%
Poultry	S.A.	M.A.	W.S.C. E.S.C. Pac. E.N.C.			
Number of farms				30,000	25,000	40,000
Per cent of all sales				70%	18%	12%
Dairy farms	E.N.C.	W.N.C.	M.A.	41,000	114,000	243,000
Number of farms						
Per cent of all sales				34%	34%	31%
Livestock except poultry and dairy	W.N.C.	E.N.C.	W.S.C. E.C.S.			
Number of farms				93,000	124,000	318,000
Per cent of all sales				55%	22%	22%
Livestock ranches	W.S.C.	Mt.	Pac.	15,000	12,000	35,000
Number of farms						
Per cent of all sales				75%	12%	13%

	General farms	W.N.C.	E.N.C.	E.S.C
Number of farms	18,000	41,000	127,000	
Per cent of all sales	37%	27%	34%	
TOTAL, ALL FARMS [e]	305,000	470,500	1,257,000	

[a] *Class*: See Table 1 for description of classes.

[b] *Type*: At least 50 per cent of the gross farm income is derived from the sale of the product designated by type name. "General farms" are those on which no one product sold provided as much as 50 per cent of the gross income. This table indicates that among all the 2 million farms that account for 94.6 per cent of the total U.S. production, specialization is well advanced and that the major share of production of each item is usually accounted for by a comparatively few farms. Tobacco is the outstanding exception.

[c] 1st, 2nd, 3rd refer to order of importance of the geographic regions in which production is concentrated. The geographic areas include the following states:

N.E. (Northeast) — Maine, N.H., Vt., Mass., R.I., Conn.
M.A. (Middle Atlantic) — N.Y., N.J., Pa.
E.N.C. (East North Central) — Ohio, Ind., Ill., Mich., Wis.
W.N.C. (West North Central) — Minn., Iowa, Mo., N. Dak., S. Dak., Nebr., Kans.
S.A. (South Atlantic) — Del., Md., D.C., Va., W. ., N.C., S. C., Ga., Fla.
E.S.C. (East South Central) — Ky., Tenn., Ala., Miss.
W.S.C. (West South Central) — Ark., La., Okla., Tex.
Mt. (Mountain) — Mont., Idaho, Wyo., Colo., N. Mex., Ariz., Utah, Nev.
Pac. (Pacific) — Wash., Oreg., Calif., Alaska, Hawaii

[d] Chiefly potatoes, hay, sugar cane, and corn not included in cash grains.

[e] Excludes 31,000 "miscellaneous" farms.

Source: *Census of Agriculture, 1959*, Vol. II, Chapter 12, Tables 54, 70–80.

TABLE 4   Changes in Numbers of Farms, by Class and Type,[a] 1950–59

(Numbers in Thousands)

Type	First and Upper Middle Class Farms (Gross Sales above $10,000)			Lower Middle Class Farms (Gross Sales $2,500 to $10,000)		
	1950	1959	Percentage Change, 1950–59	1950	1959	Percentage Change, 1950–59
Cash grain	88	149	+69.6	237	217	–8.4
Cotton	38	54	+39.3	136	105	–22.8
Other field crops[b]	18	31	+75.0	152	133	–12.5
Vegetable	8	9	+9.7	17	9	–47.1
Fruit & nut	16	28	+73.2	34	28	–17.6
Poultry	31	54	+74.0	62	40	–35.5
Dairy	71	155	+117.0	333	243	–27.0
Livestock other than poultry & dairy[c]	160	242	+51.7	365	352	–3.4
General	44	59	+12.0	250	127	–49.2

Source: Calculated from data in *Census of Agriculture, 1959,* Vol. II, Chapter 12, p. 1279.
[a] See definition of *class* as shown in Table 1. See definition of *type* in footnote b, Table 3.
[b] The census includes tobacco in this particular enumeration.
[c] The census includes ranches in this particular enumeration.

TABLE 5   Major Uses of Land, 1959 (50 states)

Major Uses	*Millions of Acres*	
AGRICULTURAL:		
Cropland harvested	317	
Cropland pastured[a]	66	
Summer fallow, idle, soil improvement crops, crop failure	75	
Sub-total		458
Pasture[b]		633
Forest[c]		
Commercial quality	530	
Non-commercial	216	
Sub-total		746
Farmsteads, barnyards, farm roads		10
Total agricultural		1,847
NON-AGRICULTURAL:		
Urban and other built-up areas	54	
Wildlife reserves, parks, recreation	62	
Public facilities: military reserves, ports, etc.	31	
Sub-total		147
Miscellaneous: desert, swamp, tundra, etc.		277[c]
Total non-agricultural		424
TOTAL LAND AREA		2,271

[a] Land suitable for cropping but presently used as pasture.

[b] 350 million acres of land in pasture and forest are considered suitable for cropland if used with proper conservation measures (see Table 7, footnote d).

[c] 215 million of these acres are in Alaska.

Source: Land and Water Resources: A Policy Guide, U. S. Department of Agriculture, May, 1962 (revised September, 1962), Tables 1 and 18.

TABLE 6   Major Classes of Land by Use and Ownership, 1959

(Million Acres)

Ownership	Cropland		Grassland Pasture and Range		Forest Land		Special Use and Other Land		Total	
	48 States	50 States	48 States	50 States	48 States[a]	50 States[a]	48 States	50 States	48 States	50 States
Federal	0.8	0.8	157.1	159.1	198.5	323.9	50.6	281.2	407.0	765.0
State and other public[b]	1.9	2.0	40.0	40.4	33.3	34.6	43.8	44.0	119.0	121.0
Private[c]	454.3	454.8	433.0	433.5	406.7	414.3	81.8	82.7	1,375.8	1,385.3
TOTAL	457.0	457.6	630.1	633.0	638.5	772.8	176.2	407.9	1,901.8	2,271.3

[a] Includes reserved forest in parks and other special uses, and Indian forest.
[b] Excludes state grant land in process of transfer from the federal public domain to the State of Alaska.
[c] Includes Indian cropland, pasture and range, special uses, and other land.
Source: Land and Water Resources: A Policy Guide, U. S. Department of Agriculture, May, 1962, p. 12.

TABLE 7   Land Capability Classes by Land Use[a]

(Thousand Acres)

Class[b]	Crop-land	Pasture and Range	Forest and Woodland	Other	Total
I	27,435	3,940	3,573	1,247	36,195
II	192,923	42,851	43,426	11,279	290,479
III	152,970	66,602	77,910	13,854	311,335
I–III	373,328	113,393	124,909	26,380	638,009
IV	48,993	53,938	58,413	7,838	169,181
I–IV[c]	422,321	167,330[d]	183,322[d]	34,218	807,190
V	1,773	10,323	28,920	1,832	43,051
VI	17,940	166,288	88,490	4,995	277,712
VII	5,636	138,690	144,227	7,682	296,233
VIII	66	2,523	6,518	18,136	27,242
V–VIII	25,415	318,025	268,154	32,645	644,238
TOTAL	447,736	485,356	451,476	66,863	1,451,428

[a] Preliminary information from the National Inventory of Soil and Water Conservation Needs for 50 states for non-federal, non-urban land.

[b] Class I — These soils have few or no conditions that limit their use. They can be safely cultivated without special conservation treatment.

Class II — These soils have some natural condition that limits the plants they can produce or that calls for some easily applied conservation practice when they are cultivated.

Class III — These soils have more serious or more numerous limitations than those in Class II. The limitations may be natural ones, such as steep slope, sandy or

Notes continued on following page

Notes to Table 7 continued

shallow soil, or too little or too much water. Or the limitation may be erosion brought on by the way the land has been used. Thus they are more restricted in the crops they can produce or, when cultivated, call for conservation practices more difficult to install or keep working efficiently.

Class IV — These soils have very severe limitations that restrict the plants they can grow or the number of years they will produce a cultivated crop. When cultivated, they require very careful management. In humid areas, they are suitable for occasional but not regular cultivation; in subhumid and semiarid areas, crops fail in low-rainfall years.

Land in the following classes generally is not suitable for cultivation but is suitable for other uses.

Class V — These soils have little or no erosion hazard but have some condition impractical to remove that limits their use largely to pasture, range, woodland, recreation, water supply, or wildlife food and cover.

Class VI — These soils have severe limitations that make them generally unsuited for cultivation and restrict their use largely to pasture, range, woodland, recreation, water supply, or wildlife food and cover.

Class VII — These soils have very severe limitations that make them unsuited for cultivation and that restrict their use to pasture, range, woodland, recreation, water supply, or wildlife food and cover with careful management.

Class VIII — These soils and land forms have limitations that prevent their use for commercial plant production and that restrict their use to recreation, water supply, or wildlife food and cover with careful protection.

[c] Total of land suitable for cropping if used with proper conservation practices. See limitations under Classes.

[d] 350 million acres now in pasture, range, and trees are suitable for cropping or occasional cropping if used with proper conservation practices.

Source: Land and Water Resources: A Policy Guide, U. S. Department of Agriculture, May, 1962 (revised September, 1962), p. 14.

TABLE 8 Projected Composition of Shifts in Major Land Uses, 1959–80

(Million Acres)

Land use shift from—	Total Reduction	Shift to—						
		Crop-land	Urban and Built-up Areas	Areas Limited Primarily to Recreation or Wildlife Use[a]	Public Installations and Facilities	Pasture and Range	Forest Land	Miscellaneous
Cropland	68	...	6	5	1	37	19	
Pasture and grazing	30	10	5	6	1	...	8	
Forest land								
Commercial	20	7	3	4	1	5	...	
Non-commercial	12	...	2	3	1	6	...	
Miscellaneous other	11	...	5	5	1	...	...	
TOTAL ADDITION	141	17	21	23	5	48	27	
NET GAIN OR LOSS		−51	+21	+23	+5	+18	−5	−11

[a] Including open space.

Source: Land and Water Resources: A Policy Guide, U. S. Department of Agriculture, May, 1962 (revised September, 1962), p. 44.

TABLE 9 Tenancy and Use of Hired Labor by Class[a] of Farm, 1959

	First Class	Upper Middle Class	Lower Middle Class	Third Class
Per cent of tenancy	23	27	24	14
Per cent that use hired help	59	28	13	4

[a] See Table 1 for description of classes.

Source: Calculated from data in the *Census of Agriculture, 1959,* Vol. II, Chapter 11, Table 5.

TABLE 10 Capital Assets, Operating Costs and Returns, 1961, by Type of Farm and Geographic Area

Type of Farms Typical of Their Areas[a]	Capital Investment per Farm	Returns per $100 Invested[b]	Per Cent of Labor Performed by Family	Hour Wage Rate of Operator after Allowing for 4.1 Per Cent Return on Capital	Net Income
Dairy farms — Central Northeast	$ 41,500	$ 3.94	81.5	$0.80	$ 4,590
Dairy farms — Eastern Wisconsin Grade A[c]	62,350	4.77	89.7	1.10	6,938
Dairy farms — Eastern Wisconsin Grade B[d]	41,170	-.20	97.5	.50	3,467
Dairy farms — Western Wisconsin Grade B	32,860	2.24	93.1	.77	4,360
Dairy-hog farms — Southeastern Minnesota	49,860	1.54	92.6	.65	4,490
Hog-dairy — Corn Belt	56,720	3.39	89.9	1.00	6,174
Hog fattening—beef raising — Corn Belt	51,500	1.11	93.2	.53	3,982
Hog-beef fattening — Corn Belt	86,770	4.38	86.9	1.20	8,126
Cash grain — Corn Belt	105,940	5.47	90.1	1.55	8,878
New Jersey, poultry producing—egg producing	44,740	1.33	82.9	.65	4,673
Delmarva, poultry producing—broilers	31,480	10.83	90.1	2.11	5,365
Cotton farms — Southern Piedmont	26,300	5.24	51.2	.60	2,671
Cotton farms — Mississippi Delta: small	13,840	6.58	69.5	.57	1,993

TABLE 10 (continued)

Type of Farms Typical of Their Areas[a]	Capital Investment per Farm	Returns per $100 Invested[b]	Per Cent of Labor Performed by Family	Hour Wage Rate of Operator after Allowing for 4.1 Per Cent Return on Capital	Net Income
Cotton farms — Mississippi Delta: large-scale	$214,440	$11.98	9.4	not applicable	$30,379
Black Prairie — Texas — cotton farms	49,630	3.93	75.2	.59	3,502
High Plains — Texas — cotton farms (non-irrigated)	60,750	19.42	68.8	4.91	13,328
High Plains — Texas — cotton farms (irrigated)	117,310	17.39	32.9	6.64	22,447
Cotton-specialty crop — San Joaquin Valley, Calif. (irrigated)	278,360	3.89	19.7	not applicable	16,324
Cotton-general crop (medium-sized) — San Joaquin Valley, Calif. (irrigated)	275,530	7.53	26.0	not applicable	25,826
Cotton-general crop (large) — San Joaquin Valley, Calif. (irrigated)	944,860	7.70	8.6	not applicable	80,904
Peanut-cotton farms — Southern Coastal Plains	17,180	15.14	76.2	1.06	3,981
Tobacco-cotton (medium-sized) — N. C. Coastal Plain	25,970	8.22	43.2	1.09	3,864

Tobacco-cotton (large) — N. C. Coastal Plain	44,880	7.71	29.0	1.29	5,275
Tobacco (small) — N. C. Coastal Plain	12,940	10.14	87.4	.93	3,234
Tobacco-livestock — Inner Area, Kentucky Bluegrass	100,170	4.72	60.0	1.14	7,451
Tobacco-dairy — Intermediate Area, Kentucky Bluegrass	22,130	-.22	94.9	.58	2,999
Tobacco-dairy — Outer Area, Kentucky Bluegrass	41,250	3.91	86.6	.81	5,122
Spring Wheat-small grain-livestock — Northern Plains	52,110	-2.78	82.0	-1.15	350
Spring Wheat-corn-livestock — Northern Plains	52,870	4.64	95.4	.95	5,753
Spring Wheat-roughage-livestock — Northern Plains	49,070	-2.66	93.4	-.26	1,423
Winter Wheat — Southern Plains	96,310	8.09	87.9	2.52	10,619
Winter Wheat-grain-sorghum — Southern Plains	89,440	10.54	91.4	3.05	12,195
Wheat-pea — Pacific Northwest	175,280	4.25	78.8	1.47	11,434
Wheat-fallow — Pacific Northwest	148,280	4.61	82.3	1.87	11,940
Cattle ranches — Northern Plains	83,890	3.72	92.0	.84	6,277
Cattle ranches — Intermountain Region	86,080	7.14	79.7	1.62	10,028
Cattle ranches — Southwest	160,700	4.05	65.5	.67	8,167
Sheep ranches — Northern Plains	96,740	3.21	55.9	.71	6,831
Sheep ranches — Southwest	205,200	3.35	41.8	.09	8,652

[a] As defined in the preface to Source reference, "typical farms are important operating units in the specified area, and in most instances they are the most common units."

[b] Operator family wage calculated at wage rate for hired help in area.

[c] Grade A is milk qualified for direct consumption as fluid Class 1 Milk

[d] Grade B is milk used for Class 2, or processor purposes.

Source: Farm Costs and Returns, Agricultural Information Bulletin No. 230, U. S. Department of Agriculture, revised October, 1962.

TABLE II   Per Cent of Farms Reporting Use of Hired
Labor, 1954–59, by Class and Type of Farm[a]

	First and Upper Middle Class Farms (Gross Sales above $10,000)		Lower Middle Class Farms (Gross Sales $2,500 to $10,000)	
Type	1954	1959	1954	1959
Cash grain	69.4	75.7	53.2	45.9
Cotton	96.8	95.4	74.6	65.6
Other field crops	95.6	95.1	81.6	76.9
Vegetables	97.8	97.3	83.1	75.8
Fruit & nut	96.4	96.5	87.8	83.6
Poultry	65.4	67.2	38.5	36.6
Dairy	83.0	78.6	56.1	51.5
Livestock, other than poultry and dairy	78.9	76.3	59.3	53.5
General	80.9	80.2	61.0	59.7

[a] *Class* is explained by Table 1. See definition of *type* in footnote b of Table 3.
Source: Census of Agriculture, 1959, Vol. II, Chapter 12, pp. 1279 and 1283.

TABLE 12   Use of *Regular* Hired Help,[a] 1954 and 1959, by Class and Type of Farm[b]

Type	Per Cent of Farms Using Regular Hired Help				Average Number of Regular Hired Help on Farms Using Regular Hired Help, by Class			
	First and Upper Middle Class		Lower Middle Class		First and Upper Middle Class		Lower Middle Class	
	1954	1959	1954	1959	1954	1959	1954	1959
Cash grain	23.8	17.7	4.1	2.4	1.6	1.6	1.2	1.2
Cotton	40.5	39.6	5.1	4.0	3.9	3.7	1.6	1.1
Other field crops[e]	41.7	32.6	5.0	4.0	3.8	3.2	1.4	1.3
Vegetable	54.4	46.2	17.2	9.9	7.6	7.7	1.4	1.5
Fruit & nut	43.8	42.0	9.0	8.2	3.9	3.8	1.4	1.4
Poultry	26.0	25.3	4.8	5.4	1.9	2.0	1.2	1.2
Dairy	48.1	36.9	10.8	7.2	2.0	1.8	1.2	1.2
Livestock other than poultry & dairy[d]	32.6	25.3	8.8	6.2	2.0	1.9	1.2	1.2
General	30.0	27.0	5.5	4.8	2.4	2.4	1.3	1.3

[a] The Census of Agriculture reports there were 700,256 *regular* hired workers on farms in 1959 and this table refers only to how 674,917 of them were distributed. These workers were less than one-sixth of all those who were employed full-time or part-time in agriculture, 1959; but the census does not report in detail by farm class and farm type how the other laborers were distributed. The entire hired farm labor force, both full-time and part-time, was about 4.5 million in 1959. That figure includes 456,000 foreign national migratory workers (chiefly Mexican) and 550,000 U. S. migratory workers. It also includes an estimated 500,000 custom workers. The entire farm family labor force, both full-time and part-time, was 5.5 million. Thus the total of the full- and part-time labor force in agriculture in 1959 was approximately 10 million — 55 per cent family and 45 per cent hired. (See U. S. Department of Agriculture: *The Hired Farm Working Force, 1959*, pp. 2, 4, 14 and *Agricultural Statistics, 1961*, p. 447.) For per cent of farms using any kind of hired labor see Table 11.

[b] For definition of *class* see Table 1. See definition of *type* in footnote b, Table 3.

[e] The census includes tobacco in this particular enumeration.

[d] The census includes ranches in this particular enumeration.

Source: *Census of Agriculture, 1959*, Vol. II, Chapter 12, p. 1284.

TABLE 13   Acreage and Capitalization of Farms, 1959, by
Class of Farm[a]

	First Class	Upper Middle Class	Lower Middle Class	Third Class
Land and buildings	$135,070	$56,846	$27,451	$11,184
Average size of farm in acres	1,338.2	444.9	241.4	85.6

[a] For definition of *class* see Table 1.
Source: Census of Agriculture, 1959, Vol. II, Chapter 11, Table 5.

TABLE 14 Commodity Credit Corporation: Net Expenditures, Fiscal Years 1952–61, and Estimated Inventories as of August 10, 1962 *(Millions of Dollars)*

Commodity	Net Expenditures, Fiscal Years 1952–61	Estimated Inventories as of Aug. 10, 1962 and Tobacco Loans as of May 31, 1962, Value
Feed grains:		
Corn	4,085.1	712.4
Grain sorghums	1,379.0	713.7
Barley	442.6	26.6
Oats and rye	148.7	12.0
Total, feed grains	6,055.4	1,464.7
Wheat and flour	9,411.6	2,104.2
Rice	773.7	.2
Other grains	163.6	115.4
Total, grains	16,404.3	3,684.5
Cotton	3,168.6	249.2
Dairy products	2,358.8	348.7
Tobacco	498.4	318.4[a]
Total of above	22,430.1	4,600.8
Interest and general overhead	2,261.3	...
Change in loans held by banks	556.2[b]	...
Bartered materials transferred to supplemental stockpile	1,008.8	...
Public Law 480 commodities not listed above and related costs not segregated by commodity (transportation estimated)	972.8	...
All other	121.5	4.2
TOTAL, CCC[d]	26,238.3[c]	4,605.0

Continued on following page

TABLE 14 (continued)

| | Total Realized Cost (Loss), Fiscal Years 1952–61 | | |
	Fiscal Year 1952	1952–61	Fiscal Year 1961
All grains	196.2	11,116.4	3,358.9
Dairy products	1.1	2,520.6	248.2
All other commodities, programs, interest and general overhead	82.8	8,468.0	1,627.0
TOTAL*	280.1	22,105.0	5,234.1

ª Loans.

ᵇ Denotes net receipts.

ᶜ Public Law 480 actual receipts from sales of foreign currencies and rentals from military housing have been credited to the commodities on a pro rata basis since the accounting records do not segregate such receipts by individual commodities.

ᵈ *Note:* Excludes special milk, National Wool Act, drought emergency feed, and other minor special programs.

ᵉ *Note:* Public Law 480 actual receipts from sales of foreign currencies and credits for currencies used in military housing construction have been credited to the commodities on a pro rata basis since the accounting records do not segregate such receipts by individual commodities.

Source: Congressional Record, August 25, 1962.

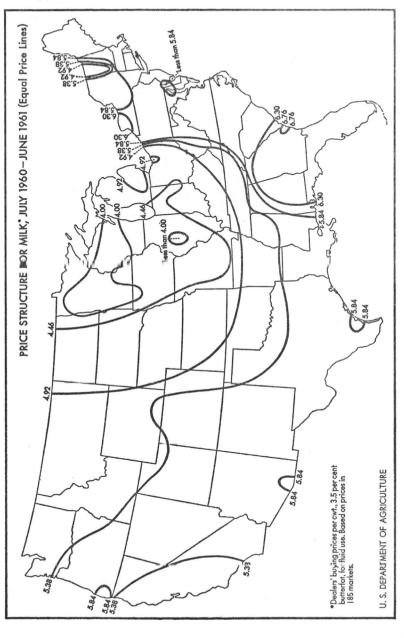

PRICE STRUCTURE FOR MILK,* JULY 1960–JUNE 1961 (Equal Price Lines)

*Dealers' buying prices per cwt., 3.5 per cent butterfat, for fluid use. Based on prices in 185 markets.

U. S. DEPARTMENT OF AGRICULTURE

MAP I

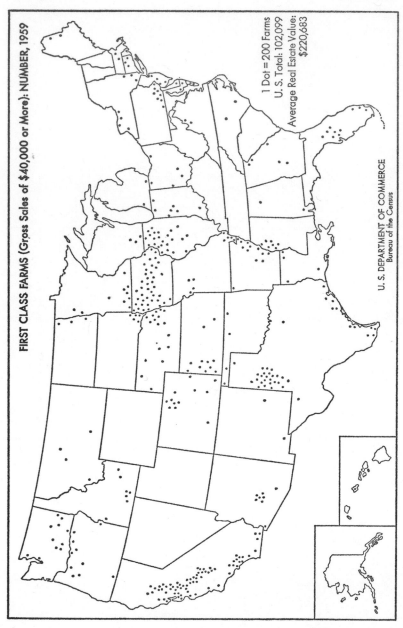

FIRST CLASS FARMS (Gross Sales of $40,000 or More): NUMBER, 1959

1 Dot = 200 Farms
U. S. Total: 102,099
Average Real Estate Value: $220,683

U. S. DEPARTMENT OF COMMERCE
Bureau of the Census

MAP 2

Index